FOUNDATIONS OF ANALYSIS

OTHER BOOKS
BY PROFESSOR LANDAU:

Differential and Integral Calculus

Elementary Number Theory

Grundlagen der Analysis

Handbuch der Lehre von der Verteilung der Primzahlen, 2 Vols.

Einführung in die Elementare und Analytische Theorie der Algebraischen Zahlen und der Ideale

Darstellung und Begründung Einiger Neuerer Ergebnisse der Funktionentheorie

Vorlesungen über Zahlentheorie, 3 Vols.

Elementare Zahlentheorie
(*Vol.* 1, *Part* 1 of Zahlentheorie)

FOUNDATIONS OF ANALYSIS

THE ARITHMETIC OF WHOLE, RATIONAL, IRRATIONAL AND COMPLEX NUMBERS

A Supplement to Text-Books on the Differential and Integral Calculus

BY

EDMUND LANDAU

TRANSLATED BY

F. STEINHARDT

COLUMBIA UNIVERSITY

CHELSEA PUBLISHING COMPANY
NEW YORK, N. Y.

THE PRESENT WORK IS A TRANSLATION INTO ENGLISH,
BY F. STEINHARDT, OF THE GERMAN-LANGUAGE BOOK
GRUNDLAGEN DER ANALYSIS,
BY EDMUND LANDAU

FIRST EDITION, 1951

SECOND EDITION, 1960

THIRD EDITION, 1966

LIBRARY OF CONGRESS CATALOGUE CARD NUMBER 60-15580

PRINTED IN THE UNITED STATES OF AMERICA

PREFACE FOR THE STUDENT

1. Please don't read the Preface for the Teacher.

2. I will ask of you only the ability to read English and to think logically—no high school mathematics, and certainly no advanced mathematics.

To prevent arguments: **A** number, **no** number, **two** cases, **all** objects of a given totality, etc. are completely unambiguous phrases. "Theorem 1," "Theorem 2," . . . . "Theorem 301" (and the like in the case of axioms, definitions, chapters, and sections) and also "1)", "2)" (used for distinguishing cases) are simply labels for distinguishing the various theorems, axioms, definitions, chapters, sections, and cases, and are more convenient for purposes of reference than if I were to speak, say, of "Theorem Light Blue," "Theorem Dark Blue," and so on. Up to "301," as a matter of fact, there would be difficulty whatever in introducing the so-called positive integers. The first difficulty—overcome in Chapter I—lies in the *totality* of the positive integers

$$1, \ldots$$

with the mysterious series of dots after the comma (in Chapter I, they are called natural numbers), in defining the arithmetical operations upon these numbers, and in the proofs of the pertinent theorems.

I develop corresponding material in each of the chapters in turn: in Chapter 1, for the natural numbers; in Chapter 2, for the positive fractions and positive rational numbers; in Chapter 3, for the positive (rational and irrational) numbers; in Chapter 4, for the real numbers (positive, negative, and zero); and in Chapter 5, for the complex numbers; thus, I speak only of such numbers as you have already dealt with in high school.

In this connection:

3. Please forget what you have learned in school; you haven't learned it.

Please keep in mind everywhere the corresponding portions of your school work; you haven't actually forgotten them.

4. The multiplication table is not to be found in this book, not even the theorem

$$2 \cdot 2 = 4;$$

but I would recommend, as an exercise in connection with Chapter 1, § 4, that you make the following definitions:

$$2 = 1 + 1,$$
$$4 = (((1 + 1) + 1) + 1),$$

and then prove the theorem.

5. Forgive me for "theeing" and "thouing" you.* One reason for my doing so is that this book is written partly *in usum delphinarum:*† for, as is well known (cf. E. Landau *Vorlesungen über Zahlentheorie,* Vol. I, p. V), my daughters have been studying (Chemistry) at the University for several semesters already and think that they have learned the differential and integral calculus in College; and yet they still don't know why

$$x \cdot y = y \cdot x.$$

Berlin, December 28, 1929.

Edmund Landau

* In the original German, Professor Landau uses the familiar "du" [thou] throughout this preface. [*Trans.*]

† For Delphin use. The Delphin classics were prepared by great French scholars for the use of the Dauphin of France, son of King Louis XIV. [*Trans.*]

PREFACE FOR THE TEACHER

This little book is a concession to those of my colleagues (unfortunately in the majority) who do **not** share my point of view on the following question.

While a rigorous and complete exposition of elementary mathematics can not, of course, be expected in the high schools, the mathematical courses in colleges and universities should acquaint the student not only with the subject matter and results of mathematics, but also with its methods of proof. Even one who studies mathematics mainly for its applications to physics and to other sciences, and who must therefore often discover auxiliary mathematical theorems for himself, can not continue to take steps securely along the path he has chosen unless he has learned how to walk—that is, unless he is able to distinguish between true and false, between supposition and proof (or, as some say so nicely, between non-rigorous and rigorous proof).

I therefore think it right—as do some of my teachers and colleagues, some authors whose writings I have found of help, and most of my students—that even in his first semester the student should learn what the basic facts are, accepted as axioms, from which mathematical analysis is developed, and how one can proceed with this development. As is well known, these axioms can be selected in various ways; so that I do not declare it to be incorrect, but only to be almost diametrically opposite to my point of view, if one postulates as axioms for real numbers many of the usual rules of arithmetic and the main theorem of this book (Theorem 205, Dedekind's Theorem). I do not, to be sure, prove the consistency of the five Peano axioms (because that can not be done), but each of them is obviously independent of the preceding ones. On the other hand, were we to adopt a large number of axioms, as mentioned above, the question would immediately occur to the student whether some of them could not be proved (a shrewd one would add: or disproved) by means of the rest of them. Since it has been known for many decades that all these additional axioms can be proved, the student should really be allowed to acquaint himself with the proofs at the beginning of his course of study—especially since they are all quite easy.

I will refrain from speaking at length about the fact that often even Dedekind's fundamental theorem (or the equivalent theorem in the development of the real numbers by means of fundamental sequences) is not included in the basic material; so that such matters as the mean-value theorem of the differential calculus, the corollary of the mean-value theorem to the effect that a function having a zero derivative in some interval is constant in that interval, or, say, the theorem that a monotonically decreasing bounded sequence of numbers converges to a limit, are given without any proof or, worse yet, with a supposed proof which in reality is no proof at all. Not only does the number of proponents of this extreme variant of the opposite point of view seem to me to be decreasing monotonically, but the limit to which, in conformity with the above-mentioned theorem, this number converges, may even be zero.

Only rarely, however, is the foundation of the natural numbers taken as the starting point. I confess that while I myself have never failed to cover the (Dedekind) theory of real numbers, in my earlier courses I assumed the properties of the integers and of the rational numbers. But the last three times I preferred to begin with the integers. For the next Spring term (as once before) I have divided my course into two simultaneous courses one of which has the title "Grundlagen der Analysis" (Foundations of Analysis). This is a concession to those hearers who want, after all, to do differentiation right away, or who do not want to learn the whole explanation of the number concept in the first semester (or perhaps not at all). In the Foundations of Analysis course I begin with the Peano axioms for the natural numbers and get through the theory of the real and of the complex numbers. The complex numbers, incidentally, are not needed by the student in his first semester, but their introduction, being quite simple, can be made without difficulty.

Now in the entire literature there is no textbook which has the sole and modest aim of laying the foundation, in the above sense, for operations with numbers. The larger books which attempt that task in their introductory chapters leave (consciously or not) quite a bit for the reader to complete.

The present book should give to any of my colleagues of the other pedagogical faction (who therefore does not go through the foundations) at least the opportunity, provided he considers this book suitable, of referring his students to a source where the material he leaves out—and that material only—is treated in full. After the first four or five rather abstract pages the reading is quite easy if—as is actually the case—one is acquainted with the results from high school.

It is not without hesitation that I publish this little book, because in so doing I publish in a field where (aside from an oral communication of Mr. Kalmár) I have nothing new to say; but nobody else has undertaken this labor which in part is rather tedious.

But the immediate cause for venturing into print was furnished by a concrete incident.

The opposition party likes to believe that the student would eventually learn these things anyway during the course of his study from some lecture or from the literature. And of these honored friends and enemies, none would have doubted that everything needed could be found in, say, my lectures. I, too, believed that. And then the following gruesome adventure happened to me. My then assistant and dear colleague Privatdozent Dr. Grandjot (now Professor at the University of Santiago) was lecturing on the foundations of analysis and using my notebook as a basis for the lectures. He returned my manuscript to me with the remark that he had found it necessary to add further axioms to Peano's in the course of the development, because the standard procedure, which I had followed, had proved to be incomplete at a certain point. Before going into details I want to mention at once that

1. Grandjot's objection was justified.
2. Axioms which, because they depend on later concepts, cannot be listed at the very beginning, are very regrettable.
3. Grandjot's axioms can all be proved (as we could have learned from Dedekind), so that everything remains based on Peano's axioms (cf. the entire following book).

There were three places where the objection came in:

I. At the definition of $x + y$ for the natural numbers.

II. At the definition of $x \cdot y$ for the natural numbers.

III. At the definition of $\sum\limits_{n=1}^{m} x_n$ and of $\prod\limits_{n=1}^{m} x_n$, after one already has $x + y$ and $x \cdot y$, for some domain of numbers.

Since the situations in all three cases are analogous, I will speak here only about the case of $x + y$ for natural numbers x, y. When I prove some theorem on natural numbers, say in a lecture on number theory, by first establishing it as true for 1 and then deducing its validity for $x + 1$ from its validity for x, then occasionally some student will raise the objection that I have not first proved the assertion for x. The objection is not justified but it is excusable; the student just had never heard of the axiom of induction. Grandjot's objection sounds similar, with the difference that it was justified; so I had to excuse it also. On the basis of his five axioms, Peano defines $x + y$ for fixed x and all y as follows:

$$x + 1 = x'$$
$$x + y' = (x + y)',$$

and he and his successors then think that $x + y$ is defined generally; for, the set of y's for which it is defined contains 1, and contains y' if it contains y.

But $x + y$ has *not* been defined.

All would be well if—and this is not done in Peano's method because order is introduced only after addition—one had the concept "numbers $\leqq y$" and could speak of the set of y's for which there is an $f(z)$, defined for $z \leqq y$, with the properties

$$f(1) = x,$$
$$f(z') = (f(z))' \qquad \text{for } z < y.$$

Dedekind's reasoning does follow these lines. With the kind help of my colleague von Neumann in Princeton I had worked out such a procedure, based on a previous introduction of ordering, for this book. This would have been somewhat inconvenient for the reader. At the last minute, however, I was informed of a much simpler proof by Dr. Kalmár in Szeged. The matter now looks so simple and the proof so similar to the other proofs in the first chapter, that not even the expert might have noticed this point had I not given above a detailed confession of crime and punishment. For $x \cdot y$ the same simple type of proof applies; however, $\sum_{n=1}^{m} x_n$ and $\prod_{n=1}^{m} x_n$ are possible only with the Dedekind procedure. But from Chap. I, § 3 on, one has the set of the $x \leqq y$ anyway.

To make it as easy as possible for the reader I have repeated in several chapters, or sometimes in all, certain (not very lengthy) phrases. For the expert it would of course be sufficient to say once and for all, for instance in the proof of Theorems **16** and **17**: This reasoning holds for every class of numbers for which the symbols $<$ and $=$ are defined and have certain properties mentioned earlier. Such repeated deductive reasonings occurred in connection with theorems which had to be given in all the chapters concerned because the theorems are used later on. But it suffices to introduce $\sum_{n=1}^{m} a_n$ and $\prod_{n=1}^{m} a_n$ since they will then apply to the preceding types of numbers. I therefore defer their introduction to the chapter on complex numbers, and do the same for the theorems on subtraction and division; the former hold for the natural numbers, say, only if the minuend is larger than the subtrahend, the latter for the natural numbers, say, only if the division leaves no remainder.

My book is written, as befits such easy material, in merciless telegram style (**"Axiom," "Definition," "Theorem," "Proof,"** occasionally **"Preliminary Remark,"** rarely words which do not belong to one of these five categories).

I hope that I have written this book, after a preparation stretching over decades, in such a way that a normal student can read it in two days. And then (since he already knows the formal rules from school) he may forget its contents, with the exception of the axiom of induction and of Dedekind's fundamental theorem.

Should, however, any of my colleagues who holds the other point of view find the matter so easy that he presents it in his lectures for beginners (in the following or in any other way), I would have achieved a success which I do not even dare hope will be realized on any large scale.

Berlin, December 28, 1929

EDMUND LANDAU

TABLE OF CONTENTS

CHAPTER V

COMPLEX NUMBERS

CHAPTER I

NATURAL NUMBERS

§ 1

Axioms

We assume the following to be given:

A set (i.e. totality) of objects called natural numbers, possessing the properties—called axioms—to be listed below.

Before formulating the axioms we make some remarks about the symbols $=$ and $\neq$ which will be used.

Unless otherwise specified, small italic letters will stand for natural numbers throughout this book.

If x is given and y is given, then

either x and y are the same number; this may be written

$$x = y$$

($=$ to be read "equals");

or x and y are not the same number; this may be written

$$x \neq y$$

($\neq$ to be read "is not equal to").

Accordingly, the following are true on purely logical grounds:

1) $$x = x$$

for every x.

2) If

$$x = y$$

then

$$y = x.$$

3) If

$$x = y, \ y = z$$

then

$$x = z.$$

Thus a statement such as

$$a = b = c = d,$$

which on the face of it means merely that

$$a = b, \quad b = c, \quad c = d,$$

contains the additional information that, say,

$$a = c, \quad a = d, \quad b = d.$$

(Similarly in the later chapters.)

Now, we assume that the set of all natural numbers has the following properties:

Axiom 1: *1 is a natural number.*

That is, our set is not empty; it contains an object called 1 (read "one").

Axiom 2: *For each x there exists exactly one natural number, called the successor of x, which will be denoted by x'.*

In the case of complicated natural numbers x, we will enclose in parentheses the number whose successor is to be written down, since otherwise ambiguities might arise. We will do the same, throughout this book, in the case of $x + y$, xy, $x - y$, $-x$, x^y, etc.

Thus, if

$$x = y$$

then

$$x' = y'.$$

Axiom 3: *We always have*

$$x' \neq 1.$$

That is, there exists no number whose successor is 1.

Axiom 4: *If*

$$x' = y'$$

then

$$x = y.$$

That is, for any given number there exists either no number or exactly one number whose successor is the given number.

Axiom 5 (Axiom of Induction): *Let there be given a set $\mathfrak{M}$ of natural numbers, with the following properties:*

I) *1 belongs to $\mathfrak{M}$.*

II) *If x belongs to $\mathfrak{M}$ then so does x'.*

Then $\mathfrak{M}$ contains all the natural numbers.

§ 2

Addition

Theorem 1: *If*

$$x \neq y$$

then

$$x' \neq y'.$$

Proof: Otherwise, we would have

$$x' = y'$$

and hence, by Axiom 4,

$$x = y.$$

Theorem 2: $$x' \neq x.$$

Proof: Let $\mathfrak{M}$ be the set of all x for which this holds true.

I) By Axiom 1 and Axiom 3,

$$1' \neq 1;$$

therefore 1 belongs to $\mathfrak{M}$.

II) If x belongs to $\mathfrak{M}$, then

$$x' \neq x,$$

and hence by Theorem 1,

$$(x')' \neq x',$$

so that x' belongs to $\mathfrak{M}$.

By Axiom 5, $\mathfrak{M}$ therefore contains all the natural numbers, i.e. we have for each x that

$$x' \neq x.$$

Theorem 3: *If*

$$x \neq 1,$$

then there exists one (hence, by Axiom 4, exactly one) *u such that*

$$x = u'.$$

Proof: Let $\mathfrak{M}$ be the set consisting of the number 1 and of all those x for which there exists such a u. (For any such x, we have of necessity that

$$x \neq 1$$

by Axiom 3.)

I) 1 belongs to $\mathfrak{M}$.

II) If x belongs to $\mathfrak{M}$, then, with u denoting the number x, we have

$$x' = u',$$

so that x' belongs to $\mathfrak{M}$.

By Axiom 5, $\mathfrak{M}$ therefore contains all the natural numbers; thus for each

$$x \neq 1$$

there exists a u such that

$$x = u'.$$

Theorem 4, and at the same time **Definition 1:** *To every pair of numbers x, y, we may assign in exactly one way a natural number, called $x + y$* (+ to be read "plus"), *such that*

1) $x + 1 = x'$ *for every x,*

2) $x + y' = (x + y)'$ *for every x and every y.*

$x + y$ is called the sum of x and y, or the number obtained by addition of y to x.

Proof: A) First we will show that for each fixed x there is at most one possibility of defining $x + y$ for all y in such a way that

$$x + 1 = x'$$

and

$$x + y' = (x + y)' \qquad \text{for every } y.$$

Let a_y and b_y be defined for all y and be such that

$$a_1 = x', \qquad b_1 = x',$$
$$a_{y'} = (a_y)', \quad b_{y'} = (b_y)' \quad \text{for every } y.$$

Let $\mathfrak{M}$ be the set of all y for which

$$a_y = b_y.$$

I)
$$a_1 = x' = b_1;$$

hence 1 belongs to $\mathfrak{M}$.

II) If y belongs to $\mathfrak{M}$, then

$$a_y = b_y,$$

hence by Axiom 2,

$$(a_y)' = (b_y)',$$

therefore

$$a_{y'} = (a_y)' = (b_y)' = b_{y'},$$

so that y' belongs to $\mathfrak{M}$.

Hence $\mathfrak{M}$ is the set of all natural numbers; i.e. for every y we have

$$a_y = b_y.$$

B) Now we will show that for each x it is actually possible to define $x + y$ for all y in such a way that

$$x + 1 = x'$$

and

$$x + y' = (x + y)' \qquad \text{for every } y.$$

Let $\mathfrak{M}$ be the set of all x for which this is possible (in exactly one way, by A)).

I) For

$$x = 1,$$

the number

$$x + y = y'$$

is as required, since

$$x + 1 = 1' = x',$$
$$x + y' = (y')' = (x + y)'.$$

Hence 1 belongs to $\mathfrak{M}$.

II) Let x belong to $\mathfrak{M}$, so that there exists an $x + y$ for all y. Then the number

$$x' + y = (x + y)'$$

is the required number for x', since

$$x' + 1 = (x + 1)' = (x')'$$

and

$$x' + y' = (x + y')' = ((x + y)')' = (x' + y)'.$$

Hence x' belongs to $\mathfrak{M}$.

Therefore $\mathfrak{M}$ contains all x.

Theorem 5 (Associative Law of Addition):

$$(x + y) + z = x + (y + z).$$

Proof: Fix x and y, and denote by $\mathfrak{M}$ the set of all z for which the assertion of the theorem holds.

I) $(x + y) + 1 = (x + y)' = x + y' = x + (y + 1)$;

thus 1 belongs to $\mathfrak{M}$.

II) Let z belong to $\mathfrak{M}$. Then

$$(x + y) + z = x + (y + z),$$

hence

$$(x + y) + z' = ((x + y) + z)' = (x + (y + z))' = x + (y + z)' = x + (y + z'),$$

so that z' belongs to $\mathfrak{M}$.

Therefore the assertion holds for all z.

Theorem 6 (Commutative Law of Addition):

$$x + y = y + x.$$

Proof: Fix y, and let $\mathfrak{M}$ be the set of all x for which the assertion holds.

I) We have

$$y + 1 = y',$$

and furthermore, by the construction in the proof of Theorem 4,

$$1 + y = y',$$

so that

$$1 + y = y + 1$$

and 1 belongs to $\mathfrak{M}$.

II) If x belongs to $\mathfrak{M}$, then

$$x + y = y + x,$$

therefore

$$(x + y)' = (y + x)' = y + x'.$$

By the construction in the proof of Theorem 4, we have

$$x' + y = (x + y)',$$

hence

$$x' + y = y + x',$$

so that x' belongs to $\mathfrak{M}$.

The assertion therefore holds for all x.

Theorem 7: $$y \neq x + y.$$

Proof: Fix x, and let $\mathfrak{M}$ be the set of all y for which the assertion holds.

I) $$1 \neq x',$$
$$1 \neq x + 1;$$

1 belongs to $\mathfrak{M}$.

II) If y belongs to $\mathfrak{M}$, then

$$y \neq x + y,$$

hence

$$y' \neq (x + y)',$$
$$y' \neq x + y',$$

so that y' belongs to $\mathfrak{M}$.

Therefore the assertion holds for all y.

Theorem 8: *If*

$$y \neq z$$

then

$$x + y \neq x + z.$$

Proof: Consider a fixed y and a fixed z such that

$$y \neq z,$$

and let $\mathfrak{M}$ be the set of all x for which

$$x + y \neq x + z.$$

I)

$$y' \neq z',$$

$$1 + y \neq 1 + z;$$

hence 1 belongs to $\mathfrak{M}$.

II) If x belongs to $\mathfrak{M}$, then

$$x + y \neq x + z,$$

hence

$$(x + y)' \neq (x + z)',$$

$$x' + y \neq x' + z,$$

so that x' belongs to $\mathfrak{M}$.

Therefore the assertion holds always.

Theorem 9: *For given x and y, exactly one of the following must be the case:*

1)

$$x = y.$$

2) *There exists a u* (exactly one, by Theorem 8) *such that*

$$x = y + u.$$

3) *There exists a v* (exactly one, by Theorem 8) *such that*

$$y = x + v.$$

Proof: A) By Theorem 7, cases 1) and 2) are incompatible. Similarly, 1) and 3) are incompatible. The incompatibility of 2) and 3) also follows from Theorem 7; for otherwise, we would have

$$x = y + u = (x + v) + u = x + (v + u) = (v + u) + x.$$

Therefore we can have at most one of the cases 1), 2) and 3).

B) Let x be fixed, and let $\mathfrak{M}$ be the set of all y for which one (hence by A), exactly one) of the cases 1), 2) and 3) obtains.

I) For $y = 1$, we have by Theorem 3 that either

$$x = 1 = y \qquad \text{(case 1))}$$

or

$$x = u' = 1 + u = y + u \qquad \text{(case 2)).}$$

Hence 1 belongs to $\mathfrak{M}$.

II) Let y belong to $\mathfrak{M}$. Then

either (case 1) for y)

$$x = y,$$

hence

$$y' = y + 1 = x + 1 \qquad \text{(case 3) for } y');$$

or (case 2) for y)

$$x = y + u,$$

hence if

$$u = 1,$$

then

$$x = y + 1 = y' \qquad \text{(case 1) for } y');$$

but if

$$u \neq 1,$$

then, by Theorem 3,

$$u = w' = 1 + w,$$

$$x = y + (1 + w) = (y + 1) + w = y' + w$$

(case 2) for y');

or (case 3) for y)

$$y = x + v,$$

hence

$$y' = (x + v)' = x + v'$$

(case 3) for y').

In any case, y' belongs to $\mathfrak{M}$.

Therefore we always have one of the cases 1), 2) and 3).

§ 3

Ordering

Definition 2: *If*

$$x = y + u$$

then

$$x > y.$$

($>$ to be read "is greater than.")

Definition 3: *If*

$$y = x + v$$

then

$$x < y.$$

($<$ to be read "is less than.")

Theorem 10: *For any given x, y, we have exactly one of the cases*

$$x = y, \quad x > y, \quad x < y.$$

Proof: Theorem 9, Definition 2 and Definition 3.

Theorem 11: *If*

$$x > y$$

then

$$y < x.$$

Proof: Each of these means that

$$x = y + u$$

for some suitable u.

Theorem 12: *If*

$$x < y$$

then

$$y > x.$$

Proof: Each of these means that

$$y = x + v$$

for some suitable v.

Definition 4: $x \geqq y$

means

$$x > y \quad or \quad x = y.$$

($\geqq$ to be read "is greater than or equal to.")

Definition 5: $x \leqq y$

means

$$x < y \quad or \quad x = y.$$

($\leqq$ to be read "is less than or equal to.")

Theorem 13: *If*

$$x \geqq y$$

then

$$y \leqq x.$$

Proof: Theorem 11.

Theorem 14: *If*

$$x \leqq y$$

then

$$y \geqq x.$$

Proof: Theorem 12.

Theorem 15 (Transitivity of Ordering): *If*

$$x < y, \quad y < z,$$

then

$$x < z.$$

Preliminary Remark: Thus if

$$x > y, \quad y > z,$$

then

$$x > z,$$

since

$$z < y, \quad y < x,$$

$$z < x;$$

but in what follows I will not even bother to write down such statements, which are obtained trivially by simply reading the formulas backwards.

Proof: With suitable v, w, we have

$$y = x + v, \quad z = y + w,$$

hence

$$z = (x + v) + w = x + (v + w),$$

$$x < z.$$

Theorem 16: *If*

$$x \leqq y, \quad y < z \quad or \quad x < y, \quad y \leqq z,$$

then

$$x < z.$$

Proof: Obvious if an equality sign holds in the hypothesis: otherwise, Theorem 15 does it.

Theorem 17: *If*

$$x \leqq y, \quad y \leqq z,$$

then

$$x \leqq z.$$

Proof: Obvious if two equality signs hold in the hypothesis; otherwise, Theorem 16 does it.

A notation such as

$$a < b \leqq c < d$$

is justified on the basis of Theorems 15 and 17. While its immediate meaning is

$$a < b, \quad b \leqq c, \quad c < d,$$

it also implies, according to these theorems, that, say

$$a < c, \quad a < d, \quad b < d.$$

(Similarly in the later chapters.)

Theorem 18: $$x + y > x.$$

Proof: $$x + y = x + y.$$

Theorem 19: *If*

$$x > y, \text{ or } x = y, \text{ or } x < y,$$

then

$$x + z > y + z, \text{ or } x + z = y + z, \text{ or } x + z < y + z,$$

respectively.

Proof: 1) If

$$x > y$$

then

$$x = y + u,$$

$$x + z = (y + u) + z = (u + y) + z = u + (y + z) = (y + z) + u,$$

$$x + z > y + z.$$

2) If

$$x = y$$

then clearly

$$x + z = y + z.$$

3) If

$$x < y$$

then

$$y > x,$$

hence, by 1),

$$y + z > x + z,$$

$$x + z < y + z.$$

Theorem 20: *If*

$$x + z > y + z, \text{ or } x + z = y + z, \text{ or } x + z < y + z,$$

then

$$x > y, \text{ or } x = y, \text{ or } x < y, \text{ respectively.}$$

Proof: Follows from Theorem 19, since the three cases are, in both instances, mutually exclusive and exhaust all possibilities.

Theorem 21: *If*

$$x > y, \quad z > u,$$

then

$$x + z > y + u.$$

Proof: By Theorem 19, we have

$$x + z > y + z$$

and

$$y + z = z + y > u + y = y + u,$$

hence

$$x + z > y + u.$$

Theorem 22: *If*

$$x \geqq y, \ z > u \text{ or } x > y, \ z \geqq u,$$

then

$$x + z > y + u.$$

Proof: Follows from Theorem 19 if an equality sign holds in the hypothesis, otherwise from Theorem 21.

Theorem 23: *If*

$$x \geqq y, \ z \geqq u,$$

then

$$x + z \geqq y + u.$$

Proof: Obvious if two equality signs hold in the hypothesis; otherwise Theorem 22 does it.

Theorem 24: $x \geqq 1.$

Proof: Either

$$x = 1$$

or

$$x = u' = u + 1 > 1.$$

Theorem 25: *If*

$$y > x$$

then

$$y \geqq x + 1.$$

Proof:

$$y = x + u,$$

$$u \geqq 1,$$

hence

$$y \geqq x + 1.$$

Theorem 26: *If*

$$y < x + 1$$

then

$$y \leqq x.$$

Proof: Otherwise we would have

$$y > x$$

and therefore, by Theorem 25,

$$y \geqq x + 1.$$

Theorem 27: *In every non-empty set of natural numbers there is a least one* (i.e. one which is less than any other number of the set).

Proof: Let $\mathfrak{N}$ be the given set, and let $\mathfrak{M}$ be the set of all x which are $\leqq$ every number of $\mathfrak{N}$.

By Theorem 24, the set $\mathfrak{M}$ contains the number 1. Not every x belongs to $\mathfrak{M}$; in fact, for each y of $\mathfrak{N}$ the number $y + 1$ does not belong to $\mathfrak{M}$, since

$$y + 1 > y.$$

Therefore there is an m in $\mathfrak{M}$ such that $m + 1$ does not belong to $\mathfrak{M}$; for otherwise, every natural number would have to belong to $\mathfrak{M}$, by Axiom 5.

Of this m I now assert that it is $\leqq$ every n of $\mathfrak{N}$, and that it belongs to $\mathfrak{N}$. The former we already know. The latter is established by an indirect argument, as follows: If m did not belong to $\mathfrak{N}$, then for each n of $\mathfrak{N}$ we would have

$$m < n,$$

hence, by Theorem 25,

$$m + 1 \leqq n;$$

thus $m + 1$ would belong to $\mathfrak{M}$, contradicting the statement above by which m was introduced.

§ 4

Multiplication

Theorem 28 and at the same time **Definition 6:** *To every pair of numbers x, y, we may assign in exactly one way a natural number, called $x \cdot y$* ($\cdot$ to be read "times"; however, the dot is usually omitted), *such that*

1) $x \cdot 1 = x$ *for every x,*
2) $x \cdot y' = x \cdot y + x$ *for every x and every y.*

$x \cdot y$ is called the product of x and y, or the number obtained from multiplication of x by y.

Proof (*mutatis mutandis*, word for word the same as that of Theorem 4): A) We will first show that for each fixed x there is at most one possibility of defining xy for all y in such a way that

$$x \cdot 1 = x$$

and

$$xy' = xy + x \text{ for every } y.$$

Let a_y and b_y be defined for all y and be such that

$$a_1 = x, \quad b_1 = x,$$
$$a_{y'} = a_y + x, \quad b_{y'} = b_y + x \text{ for every } y.$$

Let $\mathfrak{M}$ be the set of all y for which

$$a_y = b_y.$$

I) $$a_1 = x = b_1;$$

hence 1 belongs to $\mathfrak{M}$.

II) If y belongs to $\mathfrak{M}$, then

$$a_y = b_y,$$

hence

$$a_{y'} = a_y + x = b_y + x = b_{y'},$$

so that y' belongs to $\mathfrak{M}$.

Hence $\mathfrak{M}$ is the set of all natural numbers; i.e. for every y we have

$$a_y = b_y.$$

B) Now we will show that for each x, it is actually possible to define xy for all y in such a way that

$$x \cdot 1 = x$$

and

$$xy' = xy + x \text{ for every } y.$$

Let $\mathfrak{M}$ be the set of all x for which this is possible (in exactly one way, by A)).

I) For

$$x = 1,$$

the number

$$xy = y$$

is as required, since

$$x \cdot 1 = 1 = x,$$

$$xy' = y' = y + 1 = xy + x.$$

Hence 1 belongs to $\mathfrak{M}$.

II) Let x belong to $\mathfrak{M}$, so that there exists an xy for all y. Then the number

$$x'y = xy + y$$

is the required number for x', since

$$x' \cdot 1 = x \cdot 1 + 1 = x + 1 = x'$$

and

$$x'y' = xy' + y' = (xy + x) + y' = xy + (x + y') = xy + (x + y)'$$
$$= xy + (x' + y) = xy + (y + x') = (xy + y) + x' = x'y + x'.$$

Hence x' belongs to $\mathfrak{M}$.

Therefore $\mathfrak{M}$ contains all x.

Theorem 29 (Commutative Law of Multiplication):

$$xy = yx.$$

Proof: Fix y, and let $\mathfrak{M}$ be the set of all x for which the assertion holds.

I) We have

$$y \cdot 1 = y,$$

and furthermore, by the construction in the proof of Theorem 28,

$$1 \cdot y = y,$$

hence

$$1 \cdot y = y \cdot 1,$$

so that 1 belongs to $\mathfrak{M}$.

II) If x belongs to $\mathfrak{M}$, then

$$xy = yx,$$

hence

$$xy + y = yx + y = yx'.$$

By the construction in the proof of Theorem 28, we have

$$x'y = xy + y,$$

hence

$$x'y = yx',$$

so that x' belongs to $\mathfrak{M}$.

The assertion therefore holds for all x.

Theorem 30 (Distributive Law):

$$x(y + z) = xy + xz.$$

Preliminary Remark: The formula

$$(y + z)x = yx + zx$$

which results from Theorem 30 and Theorem 29, and similar analogues later on, need not be specifically formulated as theorems, nor even be set down.

Proof: Fix x and y, and let $\mathfrak{M}$ be the set of all z for which the assertion holds true.

I) $$x(y + 1) = xy' = xy + x = xy + x \cdot 1;$$

1 belongs to $\mathfrak{M}$.

II) If z belongs to $\mathfrak{M}$, then

$$x(y + z) = xy + xz,$$

hence

$$\begin{aligned} x(y + z') &= x((y + z)') = x(y + z) + x = (xy + xz) + x \\ &= xy + (xz + x) = xy + xz', \end{aligned}$$

so that z' belongs to $\mathfrak{M}$.

Therefore, the assertion always holds.

Theorem 31 (Associative Law of Multiplication):

$$(xy)z = x(yz).$$

Proof: Fix x and y, and let $\mathfrak{M}$ be the set of all z for which the assertion holds true.

I) $$(xy) \cdot 1 = xy = x(y \cdot 1);$$

hence 1 belongs to $\mathfrak{M}$.

II) Let z belong to $\mathfrak{M}$. Then

$$(xy)z = x(yz),$$

and therefore, using Theorem 30,

$$(xy)z' = (xy)z + xy = x(yz) + xy = x(yz + y) = x(yz'),$$

so that z' belongs to $\mathfrak{M}$.

Therefore $\mathfrak{M}$ contains all natural numbers.

Theorem 32: *If*

$$x > y, \text{ or } x = y, \text{ or } x < y,$$

then

$$xz > yz, \text{ or } xz = yz, \text{ or } xz < yz, \text{ respectively.}$$

Proof: 1) If

$$x > y$$

then

$$x = y + u,$$
$$xz = (y + u)z = yz + uz > yz.$$

2) If

$$x = y$$

then clearly

$$xz = yz.$$

3) If

$$x < y$$

then

$$y > x,$$

hence by 1),

$$yz > xz,$$
$$xz < yz.$$

Theorem 33: *If*

$$xz > yz, \text{ or } xz = yz, \text{ or } xz < yz,$$

then

$$x > y, \text{ or } x = y, \text{ or } x < y, \text{ respectively.}$$

Proof: Follows from Theorem 32, since the three cases are, in both instances, mutually exclusive and exhaust all possibilities.

Theorem 34: *If*

$$x > y, \ z > u,$$

then

$$xz > yu.$$

Proof: By Theorem 32, we have

$$xz > yz$$

and

$$yz = zy > uy = yu,$$

hence

$$xz > yu.$$

Theorem 35: *If*

$$x \geqq y,\ z > u \ \text{or}\ x > y,\ z \geqq u,$$

then

$$xz > yu.$$

Proof: Follows from Theorem 32 if an equality sign holds in the hypothesis; otherwise from Theorem 34.

Theorem 36: *If*

$$x \geqq y,\ z \geqq u,$$

then

$$xz \geqq yu.$$

Proof: Obvious if two equality signs hold in the hypothesis; otherwise Theorem 35 does it.

CHAPTER II

FRACTIONS

§ 1

Definition and Equivalence

Definition 7: *By a fraction* $\frac{x_1}{x_2}$ (read "x_1 over x_2") *is meant the pair of natural numbers* x_1, x_2 (in this order).

Definition 8:

$$\frac{x_1}{x_2} \sim \frac{y_1}{y_2}$$

($\sim$ to be read "equivalent") *if*

$$x_1 y_2 = y_1 x_2.$$

Theorem 37:

$$\frac{x_1}{x_2} \sim \frac{x_1}{x_2}.$$

Proof:

$$x_1 x_2 = x_1 x_2.$$

Theorem 38: *If*

$$\frac{x_1}{x_2} \sim \frac{y_1}{y_2}$$

then

$$\frac{y_1}{y_2} \sim \frac{x_1}{x_2}.$$

Proof:

$$x_1 y_2 = y_1 x_2,$$

hence

$$y_1 x_2 = x_1 y_2.$$

Theorem 39: *If*

$$\frac{x_1}{x_2} \sim \frac{y_1}{y_2}, \quad \frac{y_1}{y_2} \sim \frac{z_1}{z_2}$$

then

$$\frac{x_1}{x_2} \sim \frac{z_1}{z_2}.$$

Proof:

$$x_1 y_2 = y_1 x_2, \quad y_1 z_2 = z_1 y_2,$$

hence

$$(x_1 y_2)(y_1 z_2) = (y_1 x_2)(z_1 y_2).$$

We always have

$$(xy)(zu) = x(y(zu)) = x((yz)u) = x(u(yz)) = (xu)(yz)$$
$$= (xu)(zy);$$

therefore

$$(x_1 y_2)(y_1 z_2) = (x_1 z_2)(y_1 y_2)$$

and

$$(y_1 x_2)(z_1 y_2) = (y_1 y_2)(z_1 x_2) = (z_1 x_2)(y_1 y_2),$$

so that, by the above, we have

$$(x_1 z_2)(y_1 y_2) = (z_1 x_2)(y_1 y_2),$$
$$x_1 z_2 = z_1 x_2.$$

By Theorems 37 through 39, all fractions fall into classes, in such a way that

$$\frac{x_1}{x_2} \sim \frac{y_1}{y_2}$$

if and only if $\frac{x_1}{x_2}$ and $\frac{y_1}{y_2}$ belong to the same class.

Theorem 40: $$\frac{x_1}{x_2} \sim \frac{x_1 x}{x_2 x}.$$

Proof: $$x_1(x_2 x) = x_1(x x_2) = (x_1 x) x_2.$$

---

§ 2
Ordering

Definition 9:
$$\frac{x_1}{x_2} > \frac{y_1}{y_2}$$
(> to be read "is greater than") *if*
$$x_1 y_2 > y_1 x_2.$$

Definition 10:
$$\frac{x_1}{x_2} < \frac{y_1}{y_2}$$
(< to be read "is less than") *if*
$$x_1 y_2 < y_1 x_2.$$

Theorem 41: *If* $\frac{x_1}{x_2}, \frac{y_1}{y_2}$ *are arbitrary, then exactly one of*
$$\frac{x_1}{x_2} \sim \frac{y_1}{y_2}, \quad \frac{x_1}{x_2} > \frac{y_1}{y_2}, \quad \frac{x_1}{x_2} < \frac{y_1}{y_2}$$
is the case.

Proof: For our x_1, x_2, y_1, y_2, exactly one of
$$x_1 y_2 = y_1 x_2, \quad x_1 y_2 > y_1 x_2, \quad x_1 y_2 < y_1 x_2$$
is the case.

Theorem 42: *If*
$$\frac{x_1}{x_2} > \frac{y_1}{y_2}$$
then
$$\frac{y_1}{y_2} < \frac{x_1}{x_2}.$$

Proof: If
$$x_1 y_2 > y_1 x_2$$
then
$$y_1 x_2 < x_1 y_2.$$

Theorem 43: *If*
$$\frac{x_1}{x_2} < \frac{y_1}{y_2}$$
then
$$\frac{y_1}{y_2} > \frac{x_1}{x_2}.$$

Proof: If

$$x_1 y_2 < y_1 x_2$$

then

$$y_1 x_2 > x_1 y_2.$$

Theorem 44: *If*

$$\frac{x_1}{x_2} > \frac{y_1}{y_2}, \quad \frac{x_1}{x_2} \sim \frac{z_1}{z_2}, \quad \frac{y_1}{y_2} \sim \frac{u_1}{u_2}$$

then

$$\frac{z_1}{z_2} > \frac{u_1}{u_2}.$$

Preliminary Remark: Thus if a fraction of one class is greater than a fraction of another class, then the same will be true for all pairs of representatives of the two classes.

Proof: $y_1 u_2 = u_1 y_2, \quad z_1 x_2 = x_1 z_2, \quad x_1 y_2 > y_1 x_2,$
hence

$$(y_1 u_2)(z_1 x_2) = (u_1 y_2)(x_1 z_2),$$

and therefore, by Theorem 32,

$$(y_1 x_2)(z_1 u_2) = (u_1 z_2)(x_1 y_2) > (u_1 z_2)(y_1 x_2),$$

so that, by Theorem 33,

$$z_1 u_2 > u_1 z_2.$$

Theorem 45: *If*

$$\frac{x_1}{x_2} < \frac{y_1}{y_2}, \quad \frac{x_1}{x_2} \sim \frac{z_1}{z_2}, \quad \frac{y_1}{y_2} \sim \frac{u_1}{u_2}$$

then

$$\frac{z_1}{z_2} < \frac{u_1}{u_2}.$$

Preliminary Remark: Thus if a fraction of one class is less than a fraction of another class, then the same will be true for all pairs of representatives of the two classes.

Proof: By Theorem 43, we have

$$\frac{y_1}{y_2} > \frac{x_1}{x_2};$$

since

$$\frac{y_1}{y_2} \sim \frac{u_1}{u_2}, \quad \frac{x_1}{x_2} \sim \frac{z_1}{z_2},$$

we then have by Theorem 44 that

$$\frac{u_1}{u_2} > \frac{z_1}{z_2},$$

so that, by Theorem 42,

$$\frac{z_1}{z_2} < \frac{u_1}{u_2}.$$

Definition 11:

$$\frac{x_1}{x_2} \gtrsim \frac{y_1}{y_2}$$

means

$$\frac{x_1}{x_2} > \frac{y_1}{y_2} \quad \text{or} \quad \frac{x_1}{x_2} \sim \frac{y_1}{y_2}.$$

($\gtrsim$ to be read "greater than or equivalent with.")

Definition 12:

$$\frac{x_1}{x_2} \lesssim \frac{y_1}{y_2}$$

means

$$\frac{x_1}{x_2} < \frac{y_1}{y_2} \quad \text{or} \quad \frac{x_1}{x_2} \sim \frac{y_1}{y_2}.$$

($\lesssim$ to be read "less than or equivalent with.")

Theorem 46: *If*

$$\frac{x_1}{x_2} \gtrsim \frac{y_1}{y_2}, \quad \frac{x_1}{x_2} \sim \frac{z_1}{z_2}, \quad \frac{y_1}{y_2} \sim \frac{u_1}{u_2}$$

then

$$\frac{z_1}{z_2} \gtrsim \frac{u_1}{u_2}.$$

Proof: Obvious by Theorem 44 if $>$ holds in the hypothesis; otherwise, we have

$$\frac{z_1}{z_2} \sim \frac{x_1}{x_2} \sim \frac{y_1}{y_2} \sim \frac{u_1}{u_2}.$$

Theorem 47: *If*

$$\frac{x_1}{x_2} \lesssim \frac{y_1}{y_2}, \quad \frac{x_1}{x_2} \sim \frac{z_1}{z_2}, \quad \frac{y_1}{y_2} \sim \frac{u_1}{u_2}$$

then

$$\frac{z_1}{z_2} \lesssim \frac{u_1}{u_2}.$$

Proof: Obvious by Theorem 45 if $<$ holds in the hypothesis; otherwise, we have

$$\frac{z_1}{z_2} \sim \frac{x_1}{x_2} \sim \frac{y_1}{y_2} \sim \frac{u_1}{u_2}.$$

Theorem 48: *If*

$$\frac{x_1}{x_2} \gtrsim \frac{y_1}{y_2}$$

then

$$\frac{y_1}{y_2} \lesssim \frac{x_1}{x_2}.$$

Proof: Theorem 38 and Theorem 42.

Theorem 49: *If*

$$\frac{x_1}{x_2} \lesssim \frac{y_1}{y_2}$$

then

$$\frac{y_1}{y_2} \gtrsim \frac{x_1}{x_2}.$$

Proof: Theorem 38 and Theorem 43.

Theorem 50 (Transitivity of Ordering): *If*

$$\frac{x_1}{x_2} < \frac{y_1}{y_2}, \quad \frac{y_1}{y_2} < \frac{z_1}{z_2}$$

then

$$\frac{x_1}{x_2} < \frac{z_1}{z_2}.$$

Proof:

$$x_1 y_2 < y_1 x_2, \quad y_1 z_2 < z_1 y_2,$$

hence

$$(x_1 y_2)(y_1 z_2) < (y_1 x_2)(z_1 y_2),$$
$$(x_1 z_2)(y_1 y_2) < (z_1 x_2)(y_1 y_2),$$
$$x_1 z_2 < z_1 x_2.$$

Theorem 51: *If*

$$\frac{x_1}{x_2} \lesssim \frac{y_1}{y_2}, \quad \frac{y_1}{y_2} < \frac{z_1}{z_2} \quad or \quad \frac{x_1}{x_2} < \frac{y_1}{y_2}, \quad \frac{y_1}{y_2} \lesssim \frac{z_1}{z_2},$$

then

$$\frac{x_1}{x_2} < \frac{z_1}{z_2}.$$

Proof: Follows from Theorem 45 if an equivalence sign holds in the hypothesis; otherwise from Theorem 50.

Theorem 52: *If*

$$\frac{x_1}{x_2} \lesssim \frac{y_1}{y_2}, \quad \frac{y_1}{y_2} \lesssim \frac{z_1}{z_2}$$

then

$$\frac{x_1}{x_2} \lesssim \frac{z_1}{z_2}.$$

Proof: Follows from Theorem 39 if two equivalence signs hold in the hypothesis; otherwise from Theorem 51.

Theorem 53: *Given* $\frac{x_1}{x_2}$, *there exists a*

$$\frac{z_1}{z_2} > \frac{x_1}{x_2}.$$

Proof:

$$(x_1+x_1)x_2 = x_1x_2+x_1x_2 > x_1x_2,$$

$$\frac{x_1+x_1}{x_2} > \frac{x_1}{x_2}.$$

Theorem 54: *Given* $\frac{x_1}{x_2}$, *there exists a*

$$\frac{z_1}{z_2} < \frac{x_1}{x_2}.$$

Proof:

$$x_1x_2 < x_1x_2+x_1x_2 = x_1(x_2+x_2),$$

$$\frac{x_1}{x_2+x_2} < \frac{x_1}{x_2}.$$

Theorem 55: *If*

$$\frac{x_1}{x_2} < \frac{y_1}{y_2},$$

then there exists a $\frac{z_1}{z_2}$ *such that*

$$\frac{x_1}{x_2} < \frac{z_1}{z_2} < \frac{y_1}{y_2}.$$

Proof:

$$x_1y_2 < y_1x_2,$$

hence

$$x_1x_2+x_1y_2 < x_1x_2+y_1x_2, \quad x_1y_2+y_1y_2 < y_1x_2+y_1y_2,$$

$$x_1(x_2+y_2) < (x_1+y_1)x_2, \quad (x_1+y_1)y_2 < y_1(x_2+y_2),$$

$$\frac{x_1}{x_2} < \frac{x_1+y_1}{x_2+y_2} < \frac{y_1}{y_2}.$$

§ 3

Addition

Definition 13: *By* $\frac{x_1}{x_2}+\frac{y_1}{y_2}$ (+ to be read "plus") *is meant the fraction* $\frac{x_1y_2+y_1x_2}{x_2y_2}$.

It is called the sum of $\frac{x_1}{x_2}$ *and* $\frac{y_1}{y_2}$, *or the fraction obtained by the addition of* $\frac{y_1}{y_2}$ *to* $\frac{x_1}{x_2}$.

Theorem 56: *If*

$$\frac{x_1}{x_2}\sim\frac{y_1}{y_2},\quad \frac{z_1}{z_2}\sim\frac{u_1}{u_2}$$

then

$$\frac{x_1}{x_2}+\frac{z_1}{z_2}\sim\frac{y_1}{y_2}+\frac{u_1}{u_2}.$$

Preliminary Remark: The class of the sum thus depends only on the classes to which the "summands" belong.

Proof:
$$x_1y_2=y_1x_2,\quad z_1u_2=u_1z_2,$$
hence
$$(x_1y_2)(z_2u_2)=(y_1x_2)(z_2u_2),\quad (z_1u_2)(x_2y_2)=(u_1z_2)(x_2y_2),$$
hence
$$(x_1z_2)(y_2u_2)=(y_1u_2)(x_2z_2),\quad (z_1x_2)(y_2u_2)=(u_1y_2)(x_2z_2),$$
$$(x_1z_2)(y_2u_2)+(z_1x_2)(y_2u_2)=(y_1u_2)(x_2z_2)+(u_1y_2)(x_2z_2),$$
$$(x_1z_2+z_1x_2)(y_2u_2)=(y_1u_2+u_1y_2)(x_2z_2),$$
$$\frac{x_1z_2+z_1x_2}{x_2z_2}\sim\frac{y_1u_2+u_1y_2}{y_2u_2}.$$

Theorem 57:
$$\frac{x_1}{x}+\frac{x_2}{x}\sim\frac{x_1+x_2}{x}.$$

Proof: By Definition 13 and by Theorem 40, we have

$$\frac{x_1}{x}+\frac{x_2}{x}\sim\frac{x_1x+x_2x}{xx}\sim\frac{(x_1+x_2)x}{xx}\sim\frac{x_1+x_2}{x}.$$

Theorem 58 (Commutative Law of Addition):

$$\frac{x_1}{x_2}+\frac{y_1}{y_2}\sim\frac{y_1}{y_2}+\frac{x_1}{x_2}.$$

Proof: $\frac{x_1}{x_2} + \frac{y_1}{y_2} \sim \frac{x_1 y_2 + y_1 x_2}{x_2 y_2} \sim \frac{y_1 x_2 + x_1 y_2}{y_2 x_2} \sim \frac{y_1}{y_2} + \frac{x_1}{x_2}.$

Theorem 59 (Associative Law of Addition):

$$\left(\frac{x_1}{x_2} + \frac{y_1}{y_2}\right) + \frac{z_1}{z_2} \sim \frac{x_1}{x_2} + \left(\frac{y_1}{y_2} + \frac{z_1}{z_2}\right).$$

Proof:

$$\left(\frac{x_1}{x_2} + \frac{y_1}{y_2}\right) + \frac{z_1}{z_2} \sim \frac{x_1 y_2 + y_1 x_2}{x_2 y_2} + \frac{z_1}{z_2}$$

$$\sim \frac{(x_1 y_2 + y_1 x_2) z_2 + z_1 (x_2 y_2)}{(x_2 y_2) z_2} \sim \frac{((x_1 y_2) z_2 + (y_1 x_2) z_2) + z_1 (y_2 x_2)}{x_2 (y_2 z_2)}$$

$$\sim \frac{(x_1 (y_2 z_2) + (x_2 y_1) z_2) + (z_1 y_2) x_2}{x_2 (y_2 z_2)} \sim \frac{(x_1 (y_2 z_2) + x_2 (y_1 z_2)) + (z_1 y_2) x_2}{x_2 (y_2 z_2)}$$

$$\sim \frac{x_1 (y_2 z_2) + ((y_1 z_2) x_2 + (z_1 y_2) x_2)}{x_2 (y_2 z_2)} \sim \frac{x_1 (y_2 z_2) + (y_1 z_2 + z_1 y_2) x_2}{x_2 (y_2 z_2)}$$

$$\sim \frac{x_1}{x_2} + \frac{y_1 z_2 + z_1 y_2}{y_2 z_2} \sim \frac{x_1}{x_2} + \left(\frac{y_1}{y_2} + \frac{z_1}{z_2}\right).$$

Theorem 60:

$$\frac{x_1}{x_2} + \frac{y_1}{y_2} > \frac{x_1}{x_2}.$$

Proof:

$$x_1 y_2 + y_1 x_2 > x_1 y_2,$$

$$(x_1 y_2 + y_1 x_2) x_2 > (x_1 y_2) x_2 = x_1 (y_2 x_2) = x_1 (x_2 y_2),$$

$$\frac{x_1}{x_2} + \frac{y_1}{y_2} \sim \frac{x_1 y_2 + y_1 x_2}{x_2 y_2} > \frac{x_1}{x_2}.$$

Theorem 61: *If*

$$\frac{x_1}{x_2} > \frac{y_1}{y_2}$$

then

$$\frac{x_1}{x_2} + \frac{z_1}{z_2} > \frac{y_1}{y_2} + \frac{z_1}{z_2}.$$

Proof: If

$$x_1 y_2 > y_1 x_2$$

then

$$(x_1 y_2) z_2 > (y_1 x_2) z_2.$$

Since

$$(xy)z = x(yz) = x(zy) = (xz)y,$$

we have

$$(x_1 z_2) y_2 > (y_1 z_2) x_2$$

and

$$(z_1 x_2) y_2 = (z_1 y_2) x_2,$$

so that

$$(x_1 z_2 + z_1 x_2) y_2 > (y_1 z_2 + z_1 y_2) x_2,$$

$$(x_1 z_2 + z_1 x_2)(y_2 z_2) > (y_1 z_2 + z_1 y_2)(x_2 z_2),$$

$$\frac{x_1}{x_2}+\frac{z_1}{z_2}\sim\frac{x_1z_2+z_1x_2}{x_2z_2}>\frac{y_1z_2+z_1y_2}{y_2z_2}\sim\frac{y_1}{y_2}+\frac{z_1}{z_2}.$$

Theorem 62: *If*

$$\frac{x_1}{x_2}>\frac{y_1}{y_2}\quad or\quad\frac{x_1}{x_2}\sim\frac{y_1}{y_2}\quad or\quad\frac{x_1}{x_2}<\frac{y_1}{y_2},$$

then

$$\frac{x_1}{x_2}+\frac{z_1}{z_2}>\frac{y_1}{y_2}+\frac{z_1}{z_2}\quad or\quad\frac{x_1}{x_2}+\frac{z_1}{z_2}\sim\frac{y_1}{y_2}+\frac{z_1}{z_2}$$

$$or\quad\frac{x_1}{x_2}+\frac{z_1}{z_2}<\frac{y_1}{y_2}+\frac{z_1}{z_2},\ respectively.$$

Proof: The first part is Theorem 61; the second is contained in Theorem 56; and the third is a consequence of the first, since

$$\frac{y_1}{y_2}>\frac{x_1}{x_2},$$

$$\frac{y_1}{y_2}+\frac{z_1}{z_2}>\frac{x_1}{x_2}+\frac{z_1}{z_2},$$

$$\frac{x_1}{x_2}+\frac{z_1}{z_2}<\frac{y_1}{y_2}+\frac{z_1}{z_2}.$$

Theorem 63: *If*

$$\frac{x_1}{x_2}+\frac{z_1}{z_2}>\frac{y_1}{y_2}+\frac{z_1}{z_2}\quad or\quad\frac{x_1}{x_2}+\frac{z_1}{z_2}\sim\frac{y_1}{y_2}+\frac{z_1}{z_2}$$

$$or\quad\frac{x_1}{x_2}+\frac{z_1}{z_2}<\frac{y_1}{y_2}+\frac{z_1}{z_2},$$

then

$$\frac{x_1}{x_2}>\frac{y_1}{y_2},\ or\ \frac{x_1}{x_2}\sim\frac{y_1}{y_2},\ or\ \frac{x_1}{x_2}<\frac{y_1}{y_2},\ respectively.$$

Proof: Follows from Theorem 62, since the three cases, in both instances, are mutually exclusive and exhaust all possibilities.

Theorem 64: *If*

$$\frac{x_1}{x_2}>\frac{y_1}{y_2},\quad\frac{z_1}{z_2}>\frac{u_1}{u_2}$$

then

$$\frac{x_1}{x_2}+\frac{z_1}{z_2}>\frac{y_1}{y_2}+\frac{u_1}{u_2}.$$

Proof: By Theorem 61, we have

$$\frac{x_1}{x_2}+\frac{z_1}{z_2}>\frac{y_1}{y_2}+\frac{z_1}{z_2}$$

and

$$\frac{y_1}{y_2}+\frac{z_1}{z_2}\sim\frac{z_1}{z_2}+\frac{y_1}{y_2}>\frac{u_1}{u_2}+\frac{y_1}{y_2}\sim\frac{y_1}{y_2}+\frac{u_1}{u_2},$$

so that

$$\frac{x_1}{x_2}+\frac{z_1}{z_2}>\frac{y_1}{y_2}+\frac{u_1}{u_2}.$$

Theorem 65: *If*

$$\frac{x_1}{x_2}\gtrsim\frac{y_1}{y_2},\quad \frac{z_1}{z_2}>\frac{u_1}{u_2}\quad \textit{or}\quad \frac{x_1}{x_2}>\frac{y_1}{y_2},\quad \frac{z_1}{z_2}\gtrsim\frac{u_1}{u_2},$$

then

$$\frac{x_1}{x_2}+\frac{z_1}{z_2}>\frac{y_1}{y_2}+\frac{u_1}{u_2}.$$

Proof: Follows from Theorems 56 and 61 if the equivalence sign holds in the hypothesis; otherwise from Theorem 64.

Theorem 66: *If*

$$\frac{x_1}{x_2}\gtrsim\frac{y_1}{y_2},\quad \frac{z_1}{z_2}\gtrsim\frac{u_1}{u_2}$$

then

$$\frac{x_1}{x_2}+\frac{z_1}{z_2}\gtrsim\frac{y_1}{y_2}+\frac{u_1}{u_2}.$$

Proof: Follows from Theorem 56 if two equivalence signs hold in the hypothesis; otherwise from Theorem 65.

Theorem 67: *If*

$$\frac{x_1}{x_2}>\frac{y_1}{y_2},$$

then

$$\frac{y_1}{y_2}+\frac{u_1}{u_2}\sim\frac{x_1}{x_2}$$

has a solution $\frac{u_1}{u_2}$. *If* $\frac{v_1}{v_2}$ *and* $\frac{w_1}{w_2}$ *are solutions, then*

$$\frac{v_1}{v_2}\sim\frac{w_1}{w_2}.$$

Preliminary Remark: If

$$\frac{x_1}{x_2}\lesssim\frac{y_1}{y_2},$$

there does not exist a solution, by Theorem 60.

Proof: The second assertion of Theorem 67 is an immediate consequence of Theorem 63; for if

$$\frac{y_1}{y_2}+\frac{v_1}{v_2}\sim\frac{y_1}{y_2}+\frac{w_1}{w_2}$$

then, by Theorem 63,

$$\frac{v_1}{v_2}\sim\frac{w_1}{w_2}.$$

The existence of a $\frac{u_1}{u_2}$ (the first assertion of Theorem 67) is proved as follows. We are given that

$$x_1 y_2 > y_1 x_2.$$

Determine u from

$$x_1 y_2 = y_1 x_2 + u$$

and set

$$u_1 = u, \quad u_2 = x_2 y_2;$$

then $\frac{u_1}{u_2}$ is a solution, since

$$\frac{y_1}{y_2} + \frac{u_1}{u_2} \sim \frac{y_1}{y_2} + \frac{u}{x_2 y_2} \sim \frac{y_1 x_2}{x_2 y_2} + \frac{u}{x_2 y_2} \sim \frac{y_1 x_2 + u}{x_2 y_2} \sim \frac{x_1 y_2}{x_2 y_2} \sim \frac{x_1}{x_2}.$$

Definition 14: *The specific* $\frac{u_1}{u_2}$ *constructed in the proof of Theorem* 67 *is denoted by* $\frac{x_1}{x_2} - \frac{y_1}{y_2}$ (— to be read "minus"), *and is called the difference* $\frac{x_1}{x_2}$ *minus* $\frac{y_1}{y_2}$ *or the fraction obtained by subtraction of the fraction* $\frac{y_1}{y_2}$ *from the fraction* $\frac{x_1}{x_2}$.

Thus if

$$\frac{x_1}{x_2} \sim \frac{y_1}{y_2} + \frac{v_1}{v_2}$$

then

$$\frac{v_1}{v_2} \sim \frac{x_1}{x_2} - \frac{y_1}{y_2}.$$

§ 4

Multiplication

Definition 15: *By* $\frac{x_1}{x_2} \cdot \frac{y_1}{y_2}$ ($\cdot$ to be read "times"; however, the dot is usually omitted) *is meant the fraction* $\frac{x_1 y_1}{x_2 y_2}$.

It is called the product of $\frac{x_1}{x_2}$ *and* $\frac{y_1}{y_2}$ *, or the fraction obtained by multiplication of* $\frac{x_1}{x_2}$ *by* $\frac{y_1}{y_2}$.

Theorem 68: *If*

$$\frac{x_1}{x_2} \sim \frac{y_1}{y_2}, \quad \frac{z_1}{z_2} \sim \frac{u_1}{u_2}$$

then

$$\frac{x_1}{x_2}\frac{z_1}{z_2} \sim \frac{y_1}{y_2}\frac{u_1}{u_2}.$$

Preliminary Remark: The class of the product thus depends only on the classes to which the "factors" belong.

Proof:
$$x_1 y_2 = y_1 x_2, \quad z_1 u_2 = u_1 z_2,$$
hence

$$(x_1 y_2)(z_1 u_2) = (y_1 x_2)(u_1 z_2),$$
$$(x_1 z_1)(y_2 u_2) = (y_1 u_1)(x_2 z_2),$$
$$\frac{x_1 z_1}{x_2 z_2} \sim \frac{y_1 u_1}{y_2 u_2}.$$

Theorem 69 (Commutative Law of Multiplication):

$$\frac{x_1}{x_2}\frac{y_1}{y_2} \sim \frac{y_1}{y_2}\frac{x_1}{x_2}.$$

Proof:
$$\frac{x_1}{x_2}\frac{y_1}{y_2} \sim \frac{x_1 y_1}{x_2 y_2} \sim \frac{y_1 x_1}{y_2 x_2} \sim \frac{y_1}{y_2}\frac{x_1}{x_2}.$$

Theorem 70 (Associative Law of Multiplication):

$$\left(\frac{x_1}{x_2}\frac{y_1}{y_2}\right)\frac{z_1}{z_2} \sim \frac{x_1}{x_2}\left(\frac{y_1}{y_2}\frac{z_1}{z_2}\right).$$

Proof:

$$\left(\frac{x_1}{x_2}\frac{y_1}{y_2}\right)\frac{z_1}{z_2} \sim \frac{x_1 y_1}{x_2 y_2}\frac{z_1}{z_2} \sim \frac{(x_1 y_1) z_1}{(x_2 y_2) z_2}$$

$$\sim \frac{x_1 (y_1 z_1)}{x_2 (y_2 z_2)} \sim \frac{x_1}{x_2}\frac{y_1 z_1}{y_2 z_2} \sim \frac{x_1}{x_2}\left(\frac{y_1}{y_2}\frac{z_1}{z_2}\right).$$

Theorem 71 (Distributive Law):

$$\frac{x_1}{x_2}\left(\frac{y_1}{y_2}+\frac{z_1}{z_2}\right) \sim \frac{x_1}{x_2}\frac{y_1}{y_2}+\frac{x_1}{x_2}\frac{z_1}{z_2}.$$

Proof:

$$\frac{x_1}{x_2}\left(\frac{y_1}{y_2}+\frac{z_1}{z_2}\right) \sim \frac{x_1}{x_2}\,\frac{y_1 z_2 + z_1 y_2}{y_2 z_2} \sim \frac{x_1 (y_1 z_2 + z_1 y_2)}{x_2 (y_2 z_2)}$$

$$\sim \frac{x_1 (y_1 z_2) + x_1 (z_1 y_2)}{x_2 (y_2 z_2)} \sim \frac{x_1 (y_1 z_2)}{x_2 (y_2 z_2)} + \frac{x_1 (z_1 y_2)}{x_2 (y_2 z_2)} \sim \frac{(x_1 y_1) z_2}{(x_2 y_2) z_2} + \frac{(x_1 z_1) y_2}{(x_2 z_2) y_2}$$

$$\sim \frac{x_1 y_1}{x_2 y_2} + \frac{x_1 z_1}{x_2 z_2} \sim \frac{x_1}{x_2}\frac{y_1}{y_2}+\frac{x_1}{x_2}\frac{z_1}{z_2}.$$

Theorem 72: *If*

$$\frac{x_1}{x_2} > \frac{y_1}{y_2} \quad \textit{or} \quad \frac{x_1}{x_2} \sim \frac{y_1}{y_2} \quad \textit{or} \quad \frac{x_1}{x_2} < \frac{y_1}{y_2},$$

then

$$\frac{x_1}{x_2}\frac{z_1}{z_2} > \frac{y_1}{y_2}\frac{z_1}{z_2} \quad \textit{or} \quad \frac{x_1}{x_2}\frac{z_1}{z_2} \sim \frac{y_1}{y_2}\frac{z_1}{z_2} \quad \textit{or} \quad \frac{x_1}{x_2}\frac{z_1}{z_2} < \frac{y_1}{y_2}\frac{z_1}{z_2}, \textit{ respectively.}$$

Proof: 1) If

$$\frac{x_1}{x_2} > \frac{y_1}{y_2}$$

then

$$x_1 y_2 > y_1 x_2,$$

$$(x_1 y_2)(z_1 z_2) > (y_1 x_2)(z_1 z_2),$$

$$(x_1 z_1)(y_2 z_2) > (y_1 z_1)(x_2 z_2),$$

$$\frac{x_1}{x_2}\frac{z_1}{z_2} \sim \frac{x_1 z_1}{x_2 z_2} > \frac{y_1 z_1}{y_2 z_2} \sim \frac{y_1}{y_2}\frac{z_1}{z_2}.$$

2) If

$$\frac{x_1}{x_2} \sim \frac{y_1}{y_2}$$

then, by Theorem 68,

$$\frac{x_1}{x_2}\frac{z_1}{z_2} \sim \frac{y_1}{y_2}\frac{z_1}{z_2}.$$

3) If

$$\frac{x_1}{x_2} < \frac{y_1}{y_2}$$

then

$$\frac{y_1}{y_2} > \frac{x_1}{x_2},$$

hence, by 1),

$$\frac{y_1}{y_2}\frac{z_1}{z_2} > \frac{x_1}{x_2}\frac{z_1}{z_2},$$

$$\frac{x_1}{x_2}\frac{z_1}{z_2} < \frac{y_1}{y_2}\frac{z_1}{z_2}.$$

Theorem 73: *If*

$$\frac{x_1}{x_2}\frac{z_1}{z_2} > \frac{y_1}{y_2}\frac{z_1}{z_2} \quad \textit{or} \quad \frac{x_1}{x_2}\frac{z_1}{z_2} \sim \frac{y_1}{y_2}\frac{z_1}{z_2} \quad \textit{or} \quad \frac{x_1}{x_2}\frac{z_1}{z_2} < \frac{y_1}{y_2}\frac{z_1}{z_2},$$

then

$$\frac{x_1}{x_2} > \frac{y_1}{y_2} \quad \textit{or} \quad \frac{x_1}{x_2} \sim \frac{y_1}{y_2} \quad \textit{or} \quad \frac{x_1}{x_2} < \frac{y_1}{y_2}, \textit{ respectively.}$$

Proof: Follows from Theorem 72, since the three cases are in both instances mutually exclusive and exhaust all possibilities.

Theorem 74: *If*

$$\frac{x_1}{x_2} > \frac{y_1}{y_2}, \quad \frac{z_1}{z_2} > \frac{u_1}{u_2}$$

then

$$\frac{x_1}{x_2}\frac{z_1}{z_2} > \frac{y_1}{y_2}\frac{u_1}{u_2}.$$

Proof: By Theorem 72, we have

$$\frac{x_1}{x_2}\frac{z_1}{z_2} > \frac{y_1}{y_2}\frac{z_1}{z_2}$$

and

$$\frac{y_1}{y_2}\frac{z_1}{z_2} \sim \frac{z_1}{z_2}\frac{y_1}{y_2} > \frac{u_1}{u_2}\frac{y_1}{y_2} \sim \frac{y_1}{y_2}\frac{u_1}{u_2},$$

so that

$$\frac{x_1}{x_2}\frac{z_1}{z_2} > \frac{y_1}{y_2}\frac{u_1}{u_2}.$$

Theorem 75: *If*

$$\frac{x_1}{x_2} \gtrsim \frac{y_1}{y_2}, \quad \frac{z_1}{z_2} > \frac{u_1}{u_2} \quad \textit{or} \quad \frac{x_1}{x_2} > \frac{y_1}{y_2}, \quad \frac{z_1}{z_2} \gtrsim \frac{u_1}{u_2}$$

then

$$\frac{x_1}{x_2}\frac{z_1}{z_2} > \frac{y_1}{y_2}\frac{u_1}{u_2}.$$

Proof: Follows from Theorem 68 and Theorem 72 if the equivalence sign holds in the hypothesis; otherwise from Theorem 74.

Theorem 76: *If*

$$\frac{x_1}{x_2} \gtrsim \frac{y_1}{y_2}, \quad \frac{z_1}{z_2} \gtrsim \frac{u_1}{u_2}$$

then

$$\frac{x_1}{x_2}\frac{z_1}{z_2} \gtrsim \frac{y_1}{y_2}\frac{u_1}{u_2}.$$

Proof: Follows from Theorem 68 if two equivalence signs hold in the hypothesis; otherwise from Theorem 75.

Theorem 77: *The equivalence*

$$\frac{y_1}{y_2}\frac{u_1}{u_2} \sim \frac{x_1}{x_2},$$

where $\frac{x_1}{x_2}$ *and* $\frac{y_1}{y_2}$ *are given, has a solution* $\frac{u_1}{u_2}$. *If* $\frac{v_1}{v_2}$ *and* $\frac{w_1}{w_2}$ *are solutions, then*

$$\frac{v_1}{v_2} \sim \frac{w_1}{w_2}.$$

Proof: The second assertion of Theorem 77 is an immediate consequence of Theorem 73; for if

$$\frac{y_1}{y_2}\frac{v_1}{v_2} \sim \frac{y_1}{y_2}\frac{w_1}{w_2},$$

then, by Theorem 73,

$$\frac{v_1}{v_2} \sim \frac{w_1}{w_2}.$$

The existence of a $\frac{u_1}{u_2}$ (the first assertion of Theorem 77) is proved as follows. If we set

$$u_1 = x_1 y_2, \quad u_2 = x_2 y_1,$$

then $\frac{u_1}{u_2}$ is a solution, since

$$\frac{y_1}{y_2}\frac{u_1}{u_2} \sim \frac{u_1}{u_2}\frac{y_1}{y_2} \sim \frac{x_1 y_2}{x_2 y_1}\frac{y_1}{y_2} \sim \frac{(x_1 y_2) y_1}{(x_2 y_1) y_2} \sim \frac{x_1 (y_1 y_2)}{x_2 (y_1 y_2)} \sim \frac{x_1}{x_2}.$$

§ 5
Rational Numbers and Integers

Definition 16: *By a rational number, we mean the set of all fractions which are equivalent to some fixed fraction.* (Such a set is therefore a class in the sense of § 1.)

Capital italic letters will always denote rational numbers, unless otherwise specified.

Definition 17:
$$X = Y$$
($=$ to be read "equals") *if the two sets consist of the same fractions. Otherwise,*
$$X \neq Y$$
($\neq$ to be read "is not equal to").

The following three theorems are trivial:

Theorem 78:
$$X = X.$$

Theorem 79: *If*
$$X = Y$$
then
$$Y = X.$$

Theorem 80: *If*
$$X = Y,\ Y = Z,$$
then
$$X = Z.$$

Definition 18:
$$X > Y$$
($>$ to be read "is greater than") *if for a fraction* $\frac{x_1}{x_2}$ *of the set* X, *and for a fraction* $\frac{y_1}{y_2}$ *of the set* Y (hence for any such pair of fractions, by Theorem 44) *we have that*
$$\frac{x_1}{x_2} > \frac{y_1}{y_2}$$

Definition 19:
$$X < Y$$
($<$ to be read "is less than") *if for a fraction* $\frac{x_1}{x_2}$ *of the set* X, *and for a fraction* $\frac{y_1}{y_2}$ *of the set* Y (hence for any such pair of fractions, by Theorem 45) *we have that*
$$\frac{x_1}{x_2} < \frac{y_1}{y_2}$$

Theorem 81: *For any given X, Y, exactly one of*

$$X = Y, \; X > Y, \; X < Y$$

must be the case.

Proof: Theorem 41.

Theorem 82: *If* $X > Y$
then

$$Y < X.$$

Proof: Theorem 42.

Theorem 83: *If* $X < Y$
then

$$Y > X.$$

Proof: Theorem 43.

Definition 20: $X \geqq Y$
means

$$X > Y \text{ or } X = Y.$$

($\geqq$ to be read "is greater than or equal to.")

Definition 21: $X \leqq Y$
means

$$X < Y \text{ or } X = Y.$$

($\leqq$ to be read "is less than or equal to.")

Theorem 84: *If* $X \geqq Y$
then

$$Y \leqq X.$$

Proof: Theorem 48.

Theorem 85: *If* $X \leqq Y$
then

$$Y \geqq X.$$

Proof: Theorem 49.

Theorem 86 (Transitivity of Ordering): *If*

$$X < Y, \; Y < Z,$$

then

$$X < Z.$$

Proof: Theorem 50.

Theorem 87: *If*

$$X \leqq Y, \; Y < Z \text{ or } X < Y, \; Y \leqq Z,$$

then

$$X < Z.$$

Proof: Theorem 51.

Theorem 88: *If* $X \leqq Y,\ Y \leqq Z,$
then

$$X \leqq Z.$$

Proof: Theorem 52.

Theorem 89: *Given X, there exists a*

$$Z > X.$$

Proof: Theorem 53.

Theorem 90: *Given X, there exists a*

$$Z < X.$$

Proof: Theorem 54.

Theorem 91: *If* $X < Y,$
then there exists a Z such that

$$X < Z < Y.$$

Proof: Theorem 55.

Definition 22: *By* $X + Y$ (+ to be read "plus") *we mean the class which contains a sum* (hence, by Theorem 56, every such sum) *of a fraction from X and a fraction from Y.*

This rational number is called the sum of X and Y, or the rational number obtained from the addition of Y to X.

Theorem 92 (Commutative Law of Addition):

$$X + Y = Y + X.$$

Proof: Theorem 58.

Theorem 93 (Associative Law of Addition):

$$(X + Y) + Z = X + (Y + Z).$$

Proof: Theorem 59.

Theorem 94: $X + Y > X.$

Proof: Theorem 60.

Theorem 95: *If* $X > Y$
then

$$X + Z > Y + Z.$$

Proof: Theorem 61.

Theorem 96: *If*

$$X > Y, \text{ or } X = Y, \text{ or } X < Y,$$

then

$$X + Z > Y + Z, \text{ or } X + Z = Y + Z, \text{ or } X + Z < Y + Z,$$

respectively.

Proof: Theorem 62.

Theorem 97: *If*

$$X + Z > Y + Z, \text{ or } X + Z = Y + Z, \text{ or } X + Z < Y + Z,$$

then

$$X > Y, \text{ or } X = Y, \text{ or } X < Y, \textit{ respectively}.$$

Proof: Theorem 63.

Theorem 98: *If* $X > Y,\ Z > U,$

then

$$X + Z > Y + U.$$

Proof: Theorem 64.

Theorem 99: *If*

$$X \geqq Y,\ Z > U \text{ or } X > Y,\ Z \geqq U,$$

then

$$X + Z > Y + U.$$

Proof: Theorem 65.

Theorem 100: *If* $X \geqq Y,\ Z \geqq U,$

then

$$X + Z \geqq Y + U.$$

Proof: Theorem 66.

Theorem 101: *If* $X > Y,$

then $Y + U = X$

has exactly one solution U.

Preliminary Remark: If

$$X \leqq Y,$$

there does not exist a solution, by Theorem 94.

Proof: Theorem 67.

Definition 23: *This* U *is denoted by* $X - Y$ (— to be read "minus") *and is called the difference* X *minus* Y, *or the number obtained from subtraction of the rational number* Y *from the rational number* X.

Definition 24: *By* $X \cdot Y$ ($\cdot$ to be read "times"; however, the dot is usually omitted) *we mean the class which contains a product* (hence, by Theorem 68, every such product) *of a fraction from* X *by a fraction from* Y.

This rational number is called the product of X *by* Y, *or the rational number obtained from multiplication of* X *by* Y.

Theorem 102 (Commutative Law of Multiplication):

$$XY = YX.$$

Proof: Theorem 69.

Theorem 103 (Associative Law of Multiplication):

$$(XY)Z = X(YZ).$$

Proof: Theorem 70.

Theorem 104 (Distributive Law):

$$X(Y+Z) = XY + XZ.$$

Proof: Theorem 71.

Theorem 105: *If*

$$X > Y, \text{ or } X = Y, \text{ or } X < Y,$$

then

$$XZ > YZ, \text{ or } XZ = YZ, \text{ or } XZ < YZ, \text{ respectively.}$$

Proof: Theorem 72.

Theorem 106: *If*

$$XZ > YZ, \text{ or } XZ = YZ, \text{ or } XZ < YZ,$$

then

$$X > Y, \text{ or } X = Y, \text{ or } X < Y, \text{ respectively.}$$

Proof: Theorem 73.

Theorem 107: *If* $X > Y,\ Z > U,$

then

$$XZ > YU.$$

Proof: Theorem 74.

Theorem 108: *If*

$$X \geqq Y,\ Z > U \text{ or } X > Y,\ Z \geqq U,$$

then

$$XZ > YU.$$

Proof: Theorem 75.

Theorem 109: *If*

$$X \geqq Y,\ Z \geqq U,$$

then

$$XZ \geqq YU.$$

Proof: Theorem 76.

Theorem 110: *The equation*

$$YU = X$$

in which X and Y are given, has exactly one solution U.

Proof: Theorem 77.

Theorem 111: *If*

$$\frac{x}{1} > \frac{y}{1}, \text{ or } \frac{x}{1} \sim \frac{y}{1}, \text{ or } \frac{x}{1} < \frac{y}{1},$$

then

$$x > y, \text{ or } x = y, \text{ or } x < y, \text{ respectively,}$$

and vice versa.

Proof: $x \cdot 1 > y \cdot 1$, or $x \cdot 1 = y \cdot 1$, or $x \cdot 1 < y \cdot 1$, means the same as

$$x > y, \text{ or } x = y, \text{ or } x < y, \text{ respectively.}$$

Definition 25: *A rational number is called an integer (or a whole number) if the set of fractions which it represents contains a fraction of the form* $\frac{x}{1}$.

By Theorem 111, this x is uniquely determined. Conversely, to each x there corresponds exactly one integer.

Theorem 112:

$$\frac{x}{1} + \frac{y}{1} \sim \frac{x+y}{1},$$

$$\frac{x}{1}\frac{y}{1} \sim \frac{xy}{1}.$$

Preliminary Remark: Thus, the sum and the product of two integers are themselves integers.

Proof: 1) By Theorem 57, we have

$$\frac{x}{1} + \frac{y}{1} \sim \frac{x+y}{1}.$$

2) By Definition 15, we have

$$\frac{x}{1}\frac{y}{1} \sim \frac{xy}{1 \cdot 1} \sim \frac{xy}{1}.$$

Theorem 113: *The integers satisfy the five axioms of the natural numbers, provided that the role of* 1 *is assigned to the class of* $\frac{1}{1}$ *and that the role of successor to the class of* $\frac{x}{1}$ *is assigned to the class of* $\frac{x'}{1}$.

Proof: Let $\overline{\mathfrak{Z}}$ be the set of all integers.

1) The class of $\frac{1}{1}$ belongs to $\overline{\mathfrak{Z}}$.

2) For each integer we have defined a uniquely determined successor.

3) This successor is always different from the class of $\frac{1}{1}$, since we always have

$$x' \neq 1.$$

4) If the classes of $\frac{x'}{1}$ and of $\frac{y'}{1}$ coincide, then

$$\frac{x'}{1} \sim \frac{y'}{1},$$
$$x' = y',$$
$$x = y,$$
$$\frac{x}{1} \sim \frac{y}{1},$$

and the classes of $\frac{x}{1}$ and of $\frac{y}{1}$ coincide.

5) Let a set $\overline{\mathfrak{M}}$ of integers have the following properties:

I) The class of $\frac{1}{1}$ belongs to $\overline{\mathfrak{M}}$.

II) If the class of $\frac{x}{1}$ belongs to $\overline{\mathfrak{M}}$, then so does the class of $\frac{x'}{1}$.

Furthermore, denote by $\mathfrak{M}$ the set of all x for which the class of $\frac{x}{1}$ belongs to $\overline{\mathfrak{M}}$. Then 1 belongs to $\mathfrak{M}$, and for any x belonging to $\mathfrak{M}$, its successor x' also belongs to $\mathfrak{M}$. Therefore, every natural number belongs to $\mathfrak{M}$, so that every integer belongs to $\overline{\mathfrak{M}}$.

Since $=$, $>$, $<$, sum, and product all correspond to the earlier concepts (by Theorems 111 and 112), the integers have all the properties which we have proved, in Chapter 1, attach to the natural numbers.

Therefore, we throw out the natural numbers and replace them by the corresponding integers. Since the fractions also become superfluous, we may, and henceforth we will, speak only of rational numbers whenever any of the foregoing material is involved. (The natural numbers remain, in pairs, over and under the fraction line, in the concept of fraction; the fractions survive as individual elements of the sets which constitute the rational numbers.)

Definition 26: *The symbol* x (now freed of its previous meaning) *denotes the integer determined by the class of* $\frac{x}{1}$.

In our new terminology, we thus have, for instance,

$$X \cdot 1 = X,$$

since

$$\frac{x_1}{x_2} \cdot \frac{1}{1} \sim \frac{x_1 \cdot 1}{x_2 \cdot 1} \sim \frac{x_1}{x_2}.$$

Theorem 114: *If Z is the rational number corresponding to the fraction* $\frac{x}{y}$, *then*

$$yZ = x.$$

Proof:

$$\frac{y}{1}\,\frac{x}{y} \sim \frac{yx}{1 \cdot y} \sim \frac{xy}{1 \cdot y} \sim \frac{x}{1}.$$

Definition 27: *The U of Theorem* 110 *is called the quotient of X by Y, or the rational number obtained from division of X by Y. It will be denoted by* $\frac{X}{Y}$ (to be read "X over Y").

Let X and Y be integers, say $X = x$ and $Y = y$. Then by Theorem 114, the rational number $\frac{x}{y}$ determined by Definitions 26 and 27 stands for the class to which the fraction $\frac{x}{y}$ (in the earlier sense) belongs.

We need not be afraid of confusing the two symbols $\frac{x}{y}$, since fractions as such will from now on no longer occur. $\frac{x}{y}$ will henceforth always denote a rational number. Conversely, every rational number may be expressed in the form $\frac{x}{y}$, by Theorem 114 and Definition 27.

Theorem 115: *Let X and Y be given. Then there exists a z such that*

$$zX > Y.$$

Proof: $\frac{Y}{X}$ is a rational number; by Theorem 89, there exist integers (in our new terminology), say z and v, such that

$$\frac{z}{v} > \frac{Y}{X}.$$

By Theorem 111, we have

$$v \geqq 1,$$

hence, by Theorem 105,

$$zX = Xz = X\left(\frac{z}{v}v\right) = \left(X\frac{z}{v}\right)v \geqq \left(X\frac{z}{v}\right) \cdot 1 = X\frac{z}{v} > X\frac{Y}{X} = Y.$$

CHAPTER III

CUTS

§ 1

Definition

Definition 28: *A set of rational numbers is called a cut if*

1) *it contains a rational number, but does not contain all rational numbers;*

2) *every rational number of the set is smaller than every rational number not belonging to the set;*

3) *it does not contain a greatest rational number* (i.e. a number which is greater than any other number of the set).

We will also use the term "lower class" for such a set, and the term "upper class" for the set of all rational numbers which are not contained in the lower class. The elements of the two sets will then be called "lower numbers" and "upper numbers," respectively.

Small Greek letters will be used throughout to denote cuts, except where otherwise specified.

Definition 29:

$$\xi = \eta$$

($=$ to be read "is equal to") *if every lower number for ξ is a lower number for η and every lower number for η is a lower number for ξ.*

In other words, if the sets are identical.

Otherwise,

$$\xi \neq \eta$$

($\neq$ to be read "is not equal to").

The following three theorems are trivial:

Theorem 116:

$$\xi = \xi.$$

Theorem 117: *If*

$$\xi = \eta$$

then

$$\eta = \xi.$$

Theorem 118: *If*

$$\xi = \eta, \ \eta = \zeta,$$

then

$$\xi = \zeta.$$

Theorem 119: *If X is an upper number for ξ and if*

$$X_1 > X,$$

then X_1 is an upper number for ξ.

Proof: Follows from 2) of Definition 28.

Theorem 120: *If X is a lower number for ξ and if*

$$X_1 < X,$$

then X_1 is a lower number for ξ.

Proof: Follows from 2) of Definition 28.

Conversely, the statement of Theorem 120 is of course equivalent to 2) of Definition 28. Thus if we wish to show that a given set of rational numbers is a cut, we need show only the following:

1) The set is not empty, and there is a rational number not belonging to it.

2) With every number it contains, the set also contains all numbers smaller than that number.

3) With every number it contains, the set also contains a greater one.

§ 2

Ordering

Definition 30: *If ξ and η are cuts, then*

$$\xi > \eta$$

($>$ to be read "is greater than") *if there exists a lower number for ξ which is an upper number for η.*

Definition 31: *If ξ and η are cuts, then*

$$\xi < \eta$$

($<$ to be read "is less than") *if there exists an upper number for ξ which is a lower number for η.*

Theorem 121: *If*

$$\xi > \eta$$

then

$$\eta < \xi.$$

Proof: Each means that there exists an upper number for η which is a lower number for ξ.

Theorem 122: *If*

$$\xi < \eta$$

then

$$\eta > \xi.$$

Proof: Each means that there exists a lower number for η which is an upper number for ξ.

Theorem 123: *For any given ξ, η, exactly one of*

$$\xi = \eta, \ \xi > \eta, \ \xi < \eta$$

is the case.

Proof: 1)

$$\xi = \eta, \ \xi > \eta$$

are incompatible by Definition 29 and Definition 30.

$$\xi = \eta, \ \xi < \eta$$

are incompatible by Definition 29 and Definition 31.

If we had

$$\xi > \eta, \ \xi < \eta,$$

it would follow that there exists a lower number X for ξ which is an upper number for η, and that there also exists an upper number Y for ξ which is a lower number for η. By 2) of Definition 28, we would then have both

$$X < Y \text{ and } X > Y.$$

Therefore we can have at most one of the three cases.

2) If

$$\xi \neq \eta,$$

then the lower classes do not coincide. Then we either have that some lower number for ξ is an upper number for η, in which case it follows that

$$\xi > \eta;$$

or we have that some lower number for η is an upper number for ξ, in which case it follows that

$$\xi < \eta.$$

Definition 32:

$$\xi \geqq \eta$$

means

$$\xi > \eta \text{ or } \xi = \eta.$$

($\geqq$ to be read "is greater than or equal to.")

Definition 33:

$$\xi \leqq \eta$$

means

$$\xi < \eta \text{ or } \xi = \eta.$$

($\leqq$ to be read "is less than or equal to.")

Theorem 124: *If*

$$\xi \geqq \eta$$

then

$$\eta \leqq \xi.$$

Proof: Theorem 121.

Theorem 125: *If*

$$\xi \leqq \eta$$

then

$$\eta \geqq \xi.$$

Proof: Theorem 122.

Theorem 126 (Transitivity of Ordering): *If*

$$\xi < \eta, \ \eta < \zeta,$$

then

$$\xi < \zeta.$$

Proof: There exists an upper number X for ξ which is a lower number for η; there also exists an upper number Y for η which is a lower number for ζ. Applying property 2) of cuts (cf. Definition 28) to the cut η, we obtain

$$X < Y,$$

so that Y is an upper number for ξ. Therefore

$$\xi < \zeta.$$

Theorem 127: *If*

$$\xi \leqq \eta, \ \eta < \zeta \ \textit{or} \ \xi < \eta, \ \eta \leqq \zeta,$$

then

$$\xi < \zeta.$$

Proof: Obvious if the equality sign holds in the hypothesis; otherwise, Theorem 126 does it.

Theorem 128: *If*

$$\xi \leqq \eta, \ \eta \leqq \zeta,$$

then

$$\xi \leqq \zeta.$$

Proof: Obvious if two equality signs hold in the hypothesis; otherwise, Theorem 127 does it.

§ 3

Addition

Theorem 129: I) *Let ξ and η be cuts. Then the set of all rational numbers which are representable in the form $X + Y$, where X is a lower number for ξ and Y is a lower number for η, is itself a cut.*

II) *No number of this set can be written as a sum of an upper number for ξ and an upper number for η.*

Proof: 1) Consider any lower number X for ξ and any lower number Y for η. Then $X + Y$ belongs to our set.

Next, consider any upper number X_1 for ξ and any upper number Y_1 for η; if X and Y are any lower numbers for ξ and for η respectively, we have

$$X < X_1, \quad Y < Y_1,$$

hence

$$X + Y < X_1 + Y_1,$$
$$X_1 + Y_1 \neq X + Y;$$

therefore $X_1 + Y_1$ does not belong to our set, and we have proved II), as well as property 1) of cuts for our set.

2) To prove that our set satisfies property 2) of cuts, we must show that with any number it contains, our set also contains all numbers which are less than that number. Let

$$Z < X + Y,$$

where X and Y are lower numbers for ξ and η respectively. Then

$$(X + Y)\frac{Z}{X+Y} < (X+Y)\cdot 1,$$

hence, by Theorem 106,

$$\frac{Z}{X+Y} < 1,$$

so that, by Theorem 105,

$$X\frac{Z}{X+Y} < X\cdot 1 = X$$

and

$$Y\frac{Z}{X+Y} < Y\cdot 1 = Y;$$

therefore by virtue of the second property of cuts as applied to ξ and η, the numbers $X\frac{Z}{X+Y}$ and $Y\frac{Z}{X+Y}$ are lower numbers for ξ and η respectively.

The sum of those two rational numbers is the given Z, since

$$X\frac{Z}{X+Y}+Y\frac{Z}{X+Y}=(X+Y)\frac{Z}{X+Y}=Z.$$

3) Any given number of our set is of the form $X+Y$ where X and Y are lower numbers for ξ and η respectively. Using the third property of cuts as applied to ξ, we can find a lower number

$$X_1>X$$

for ξ; then

$$X_1+Y>X+Y,$$

so that there exists in our set a number which is $>X+Y$.

Definition 34: *The cut constructed in Theorem* 129 *is denoted by* $\xi+\eta$ (+ to be read "plus") *and is called the sum of* ξ *and* η, *or the cut obtained from addition of* η *to* ξ.

Theorem 130 (Commutative Law of Addition):

$$\xi+\eta=\eta+\xi.$$

Proof: Every $X+Y$ is a $Y+X$, and vice versa.

Theorem 131 (Associative Law of Addition):

$$(\xi+\eta)+\zeta=\xi+(\eta+\zeta).$$

Proof: Every $(X+Y)+Z$ is an $X+(Y+Z)$, and vice versa.

Theorem 132: *Given any* A, *and given a cut, then there exist a lower number* X *and an upper number* U *for the cut such that*

$$U-X=A.$$

Proof: Let X_1 be some lower number, and consider all rational numbers

$$X_1+nA$$

where n is an integer. Not all of these are lower numbers; for if Y is any upper number, then

$$Y>X_1;$$

hence by Theorem 115, we have for some suitable n that

$$nA>Y-X_1,$$

$$X_1+nA>(Y-X_1)+X_1=Y,$$

so that X_1+nA is an upper number.

The set of all n for which $X_1 + nA$ is an upper number contains a smallest integer, by Theorem 27; we will denote it by u.

If

$$u = 1,$$

then we set

$$X = X_1, \quad U = X_1 + A;$$

if

$$u > 1,$$

then we set

$$X = X_1 + (u - 1)A, \quad U = X_1 + uA = X + A.$$

In each case, X is a lower and U an upper number, and

$$U - X = A.$$

Theorem 133: $\xi + \eta > \xi.$

Proof: Let Y be a lower number for η. By Theorem 132, we can find a lower number X for ξ and an upper number U for ξ such that

$$U - X = Y;$$

then the number

$$U = X + Y$$

is an upper number for ξ and a lower number for $\xi + \eta$. Therefore

$$\xi + \eta > \xi.$$

Theorem 134: *If* $\xi > \eta$

then

$$\xi + \zeta > \eta + \zeta.$$

Proof: There exists an upper number Y for η which is a lower number for ξ. Choose a greater lower number

$$X > Y$$

for ξ; it is an upper number for η. Now by Theorem 132, we can find an upper number Z for ζ and a lower number U for ζ such that

$$Z - U = X - Y.$$

Then we have

$$Y + Z = Y + ((X - Y) + U) = (Y + (X - Y)) + U = X + U,$$

so that this number, besides being a lower number for $\xi + \zeta$, is also (by Theorem 129, II)) an upper number for $\eta + \zeta$. Therefore

$$\xi + \zeta > \eta + \zeta.$$

Theorem 135: *If*

$$\xi > \eta, \text{ or } \xi = \eta, \text{ or } \xi < \eta,$$

then

$$\xi + \zeta > \eta + \zeta, \text{ or } \xi + \zeta = \eta + \zeta, \text{ or } \xi + \zeta < \eta + \zeta,$$

respectively.

Proof: The first part is Theorem 134, the second is obvious, and the third follows from the first since

$$\eta > \xi,$$

$$\eta + \zeta > \xi + \zeta,$$

$$\xi + \zeta < \eta + \zeta.$$

Theorem 136: *If*

$$\xi + \zeta > \eta + \zeta, \text{ or } \xi + \zeta = \eta + \zeta, \text{ or } \xi + \zeta < \eta + \zeta,$$

then

$$\xi > \eta, \text{ or } \xi = \eta, \text{ or } \xi < \eta, \text{ respectively.}$$

Proof: Follows from Theorem 135, since the three cases are, in both instances, mutually exclusive and exhaust all possibilities.

Theorem 137: *If*

$$\xi > \eta, \quad \zeta > \upsilon$$

then

$$\xi + \zeta > \eta + \upsilon.$$

Proof: By Theorem 134, we have

$$\xi + \zeta > \eta + \zeta$$

and

$$\eta + \zeta = \zeta + \eta > \upsilon + \eta = \eta + \upsilon,$$

so that

$$\xi + \zeta > \eta + \upsilon.$$

Theorem 138: *If*

$$\xi \geqq \eta, \ \zeta > \upsilon \text{ or } \xi > \eta, \ \zeta \geqq \upsilon$$

then

$$\xi + \zeta > \eta + \upsilon.$$

Proof: Follows from Theorem 134 if the equality sign holds in the hypothesis; otherwise from Theorem 137.

Theorem 139: *If*

$$\xi \geqq \eta, \quad \zeta \geqq \upsilon$$

then

$$\xi + \zeta \geqq \eta + \upsilon.$$

Proof: Obvious if two equality signs hold in the hypothesis; otherwise, Theorem 138 does it.

Theorem 140: *If*

$$\xi > \eta,$$

then

$$\eta + \upsilon = \xi$$

has exactly one solution υ.

Preliminary Remark: If

$$\xi \leqq \eta,$$

then there does not exist a solution, by Theorem 133.

Proof: I) There exists at most one solution; for if

$$\upsilon_1 \neq \upsilon_2$$

then, by Theorem 135,

$$\eta + \upsilon_1 \neq \eta + \upsilon_2.$$

II) I will show first that the set of all rational numbers of the form $X - Y$ (hence $X > Y$) where X is a lower number for ξ and Y is an upper number for η, constitutes a cut.

1) We know from the first part of the proof of Theorem 134 that such an $X - Y$ does indeed exist.

No upper number X_1 for ξ can constitute such an $X - Y$, since each number of this form satisfies

$$X - Y < (X - Y) + Y = X < X_1.$$

2) If an $X - Y$ of the above sort is given and if

$$U < X - Y,$$

then

$$U + Y < (X - Y) + Y = X,$$

so that the number

$$U + Y = X_2$$

is a lower number for ξ, and the number

$$U = X_2 - Y$$

belongs to our set.

3) If an $X - Y$ of the above sort is given, choose a lower number

$$X_3 > X$$

for ξ. Then

$$(X_3 - Y) + Y > (X - Y) + Y,$$
$$X_3 - Y > X - Y,$$

so that $X_3 - Y$ is a number of our set which is greater than the given number $X - Y$.

Our set is therefore a cut; let us denote it by υ.

We will show that it satisfies

$$\eta + \upsilon = \xi.$$

To prove this, it suffices to establish the following two statements:

A) Every lower number for $\upsilon + \eta$ is a lower number for ξ.

B) Every lower number for ξ is a lower number for $\upsilon + \eta$.

As regards A): Every lower number for $\upsilon + \eta$ is of the form

$$(X - Y) + Y_1$$

where X is a lower number for ξ, Y an upper number foı η, Y_1 a lower number for η, and

$$X > Y.$$

Now we have

$$Y > Y_1,$$

$$((X-Y)+Y_1)+(Y-Y_1) = (X-Y)+(Y_1+(Y-Y_1)) = (X-Y)+Y = X,$$

$$(X-Y)+Y_1 < X,$$

so that $(X - Y) + Y_1$ is a lower number for ξ.

As regards B): a) Let the given lower number for ξ be at the same time an upper number for η, and denote it by Y. Choose a lower number X for ξ such that

$$X > Y,$$

and moreover choose, by Theorem 132, a lower number Y_1 for η and an upper number Y_2 for η such that

$$Y_2 - Y_1 = X - Y.$$

Then we have

$$Y > Y_1,$$

hence

$$Y_2 + (Y - Y_1) = ((X-Y)+Y_1)+(Y-Y_1) = (X-Y)+(Y_1+(Y-Y_1))$$
$$= (X-Y)+Y = X,$$

$$Y - Y_1 = X - Y_2,$$

$$Y = (Y-Y_1)+Y_1 = (X-Y_2)+Y_1,$$

so that Y is a lower number for $\upsilon + \eta$.

b) If the given lower number for ξ is also a lower number for η, then it is less than all those rational numbers which were considered in a) and which turned out to be lower numbers for $\upsilon + \eta$. Hence in this case the given number must itself be a lower number for $\upsilon + \eta$.

Definition 35: *The* υ *of Theorem* 140 *is denoted by* $\xi - \eta$ (— to be read "minus") *and is called the difference* ξ *minus* η, *or the cut obtained by subtraction of* η *from* ξ.

§ 4

Multiplication

Theorem 141: I) *Let ξ and η be cuts. Then the set of all rational numbers which are representable in the form XY, where X is a lower number for ξ and Y is a lower number for η, is itself a cut.*

II) *No number of this set can be written as a product of an upper number for ξ and an upper number for η.*

Proof: 1) Consider any lower number X for ξ and any lower number Y for η; then XY belongs to the set.

Next, consider any upper number X_1 for ξ and any upper number Y_1 for η. If X and Y are any lower numbers for ξ and for η respectively, we have

$$X < X_1, \quad Y < Y_1,$$

hence

$$XY < X_1 Y_1,$$

$$X_1 Y_1 \neq XY;$$

therefore X_1Y_1 does not belong to our set, and we have proved II), as well as property 1) of cuts, for our set.

2) Let X be a lower number for ξ, Y a lower number for η, and let

$$Z < XY.$$

Then we have

$$X\left(\frac{1}{X} Z\right) = \left(X \frac{1}{X}\right) Z = 1 \cdot Z = Z,$$

$$\frac{Z}{X} = \frac{1}{X} Z < \frac{1}{X}(XY) = \left(\frac{1}{X} X\right) Y = Y,$$

so that $\frac{Z}{X}$ is a lower number for η. The equation

$$Z = X \frac{Z}{X}$$

thus shows that Z belongs to our set.

3) Let there be given any number of the set; it is of the form XY where X and Y are lower numbers for ξ and for η respectively. Choose a lower number

$$X_1 > X$$

for ξ; then we have that

$$X_1Y > XY,$$

so that our set contains a number which is $> XY$.

Definition 36: *The cut constructed in Theorem* 141 *is denoted by* $\xi \cdot \eta$ ($\cdot$ to be read "times"; however the dot is usually omitted), *and is called the product of* ξ *and* η, *or the cut obtained from multiplication of* ξ *by* η.

Theorem 142 (Commutative Law of Multiplication):

$$\xi\eta = \eta\xi.$$

Proof: Every XY is a YX, and vice versa.

Theorem 143 (Associative Law of Multiplication):

$$(\xi\eta)\zeta = \xi(\eta\zeta).$$

Proof: Every $(XY)Z$ is an $X(YZ)$, and vice versa.

Theorem 144 (Distributive Law):

$$\xi(\eta + \zeta) = \xi\eta + \xi\zeta.$$

Proof: I) Every lower number for $\xi(\eta + \zeta)$ is of the form

$$X(Y + Z) = XY + XZ$$

where X, Y and Z are lower numbers for ξ, η, and ζ, respectively. The number $XY + XZ$ is a lower number for $\xi\eta + \xi\zeta$.

II) Every lower number for $\xi\eta + \xi\zeta$ is of the form

$$XY + X_1Z$$

where X, Y, X_1, and Z are lower numbers for ξ, η, ξ, and ζ, respectively. Let X_2 stand for the number X in case $X \geqq X_1$ and for the number X_1 in case $X < X_1$; then X_2 is a lower number for ξ, so that $X_2(Y + Z)$ is a lower number for $\xi(\eta + \zeta)$. From

$$XY \leqq X_2Y,$$
$$X_1Z \leqq X_2Z$$

follows

$$XY + X_1Z \leqq X_2Y + X_2Z = X_2(Y + Z);$$

hence $XY + X_1Z$ is a lower number for $\xi(\eta + \zeta)$.

Theorem 145: *If*

$$\xi > \eta, \text{ or } \xi = \eta, \text{ or } \xi < \eta,$$

then

$$\xi\zeta > \eta\zeta, \text{ or } \xi\zeta = \eta\zeta, \text{ or } \xi\zeta < \eta\zeta, \text{ respectively.}$$

Proof: 1) If

$$\xi > \eta,$$

then we have by Theorem 140 that, with a suitable v,

$$\xi = \eta + v,$$

hence

$$\xi\zeta = (\eta + v)\zeta = \eta\zeta + v\zeta > \eta\zeta.$$

2) If

$$\xi = \eta$$

then obviously

$$\xi\zeta = \eta\zeta.$$

3) If

$$\xi < \eta$$

then

$$\eta > \xi,$$

so that by 1),

$$\eta\zeta > \xi\zeta,$$
$$\xi\zeta < \eta\zeta.$$

Theorem 146: *If*

$$\xi\zeta > \eta\zeta, \text{ or } \xi\zeta = \eta\zeta, \text{ or } \xi\zeta < \eta\zeta,$$

then

$$\xi > \eta, \text{ or } \xi = \eta, \text{ or } \xi < \eta, \textit{ respectively.}$$

Proof: Follows from Theorem 145, since the three cases are, in both instances, mutually exclusive and exhaust all possibilities.

Theorem 147: *If*

$$\xi > \eta, \; \zeta > v$$

then

$$\xi\zeta > \eta v.$$

Proof: By Theorem 145,

$$\xi\zeta > \eta\zeta$$

and

$$\eta\zeta = \zeta\eta > v\eta = \eta v,$$

so that

$$\xi\zeta > \eta v.$$

Theorem 148: *If*

$$\xi \geqq \eta, \; \zeta > v \text{ or } \xi > \eta, \; \zeta \geqq v,$$

then

$$\xi\zeta > \eta v.$$

Proof: Follows from Theorem 145 if an equality sign holds in the hypothesis; otherwise from Theorem 147.

Theorem 149: *If*

$$\xi \geqq \eta, \; \zeta \geqq v,$$

then

$$\xi\zeta \geqq \eta v.$$

Proof: Obvious if two equality signs hold in the hypothesis; otherwise, Theorem 148 does it.

Theorem 150: *For any given rational number R, the set of all rational numbers $< R$ constitutes a cut.*

Proof: 1) By Theorem 90, there does exist an $X < R$. The number R itself is not $< R$.

2) If

$$X < R,\ X_1 \geqq R,$$

then

$$X < X_1.$$

3) If

$$X < R,$$

then by Theorem 91 there exists an X_1 such that

$$X < X_1 < R.$$

Definition 37: *The cut constructed in Theorem* 150 *is denoted by R^*.*

(Thus capital italic letters with asterisks will stand for cuts, not for rational numbers.)

Theorem 151: $$\xi \cdot 1^* = \xi.$$

Proof: $\xi \cdot 1^*$ is the set of all XY where X is a lower number for ξ and

$$Y < 1.$$

Every such XY is $< X$ and thus is a lower number for ξ.

Conversely, let there be given a lower number X for ξ. Choose, for ξ, a lower number

$$X_1 > X$$

and set

$$Y = \frac{1}{X_1}X.$$

Then

$$Y < \frac{1}{X_1}X_1 = 1,$$

so that the number

$$X = X_1 Y$$

is a lower number for $\xi \cdot 1^*$.

Theorem 152: *For any given ξ, the equation*

$$\xi v = 1^*$$

has a solution v.

Proof: Consider the set of all numbers $\frac{1}{X}$ where X may be any upper number for ξ, excepting only the least upper number (if such a one exists). We will show that this set is a cut.

1) The set does contain a number; for if X is an upper number for ξ, then so is $X + X$, and the latter indeed can not be the smallest, so that $\frac{1}{X+X}$ belongs to our set.

There exists a rational number which does not belong to the set; for if X_1 is any lower number for ξ, then any upper number X for ξ satisfies

$$X \neq X_1,$$

hence, since

$$X\frac{1}{X} = 1 = X_1\frac{1}{X_1},$$

$$\frac{1}{X} \neq \frac{1}{X_1};$$

thus $\frac{1}{X_1}$ does not belong to our set.

2) Consider any number $\frac{1}{X}$ of our set; then X is an upper number for ξ. Now if

$$U < \frac{1}{X},$$

then

$$UX < \frac{1}{X}X = 1 = U\frac{1}{U},$$

hence

$$X < \frac{1}{U},$$

so that $\frac{1}{U}$ is an upper number for ξ, and is not the least such. Since

$$U\frac{1}{U} = 1,$$

$$U = \frac{1}{\frac{1}{U}},$$

the number U belongs to our set.

3) Let there be given a number $\frac{1}{X}$ of our set; then X is an upper number for ξ, and is not the least such. Choose an upper number

$$X_1 < X$$

for ξ, and choose (Theorem 91) an X_2 such that

$$X_1 < X_2 < X.$$

Then X_2 is an upper number for ξ, and is not the least such. From

$$X_2 \frac{1}{X} < X \frac{1}{X} = 1 = X_2 \frac{1}{X_2}$$

we obtain

$$\frac{1}{X_2} > \frac{1}{X},$$

so that we have found a number in our set which is greater than the given one.

Our set is therefore a cut; let it be denoted by v.

We will show that it satisfies.

$$\xi v = 1^*.$$

To prove this, it suffices to establish the following two statements:

A) Every lower number for ξv is < 1.

B) Every rational number < 1 is a lower number for ξv.

As regards A): Every lower number for ξv is of the form

$$X \frac{1}{X_1},$$

where X is a lower number for ξ and X_1 an upper number for ξ. Now

$$X < X_1$$

implies

$$X \frac{1}{X_1} < X_1 \frac{1}{X_1} = 1.$$

As regards B): Let

$$U < 1.$$

Choose any lower number X for ξ and then, by Theorem 132, a lower number X_1 for ξ and an upper number X_2 for ξ such that

$$X_2 - X_1 = (1 - U) X.$$

Then we have

$$X_2 - X_1 < (1 - U) X_2,$$

$$(X_2 - X_1) + UX_2 < (1 - U) X_2 + UX_2 = X_2 = (X_2 - X_1) + X_1,$$

$$UX_2 < X_1,$$

$$X_2 = \left(\frac{1}{U} U\right) X_2 = \frac{1}{U}(UX_2) < \frac{1}{U} X_1 = \frac{X_1}{U}.$$

Therefore $\frac{X_1}{U}$ is an upper number for ξ, and is not the least such.

If

$$U\frac{X_1}{U} = X_1$$

then

$$U = \frac{X_1}{\frac{X_1}{U}} = X_1 \frac{1}{\frac{X_1}{U}};$$

here, X_1 is a lower number for ξ, and $\dfrac{1}{\frac{X_1}{U}}$ is a lower number for v; hence U is a lower number for ξv.

Theorem 153: *The equation*

$$\eta v = \xi,$$

where ξ and η are given, has exactly one solution v.

Proof: I) There exists at most one solution; for if

$$v_1 \neq v_2$$

then, by Theorem 145,

$$\eta v_1 \neq \eta v_2.$$

II) If τ is the solution—whose existence is proved by Theorem 152—of the equation

$$\eta \tau = 1^*,$$

then the cut

$$v = \tau \xi$$

satisfies the equation in Theorem 153; for we have, by Theorem 151, that

$$\eta v = \eta(\tau\xi) = (\eta\tau)\xi = 1^*\xi = \xi.$$

Definition 38: *The v of Theorem 153 is denoted by* $\dfrac{\xi}{\eta}$ (to be read "ξ over η"), *and is called the quotient of ξ by η, or the cut obtained from division of ξ by η.*

§ 5
Rational Cuts and Integral Cuts

Definition 39: *A cut of the form X^* is called a rational cut.*

Definition 40: *A cut of the form x^* is called an integral cut.*

(Thus small italic letters with asterisks stand for cuts, not for integers.)

Theorem 154: *If*

$$X > Y, \text{ or } X = Y, \text{ or } X < Y,$$

then

$$X^* > Y^*, \text{ or } X^* = Y^*, \text{ or } X^* < Y^*, \text{ respectively,}$$

and vice versa.

Proof: I) 1) If

$$X > Y,$$

then Y is a lower number for X^*. The number Y is an upper number for Y^*. Therefore

$$X^* > Y^*.$$

2) If

$$X = Y$$

then clearly

$$X^* = Y^*.$$

3) If

$$X < Y$$

then

$$Y > X,$$

hence, by 1),

$$Y^* > X^*,$$

$$X^* < Y^*.$$

II) The converse is obvious, since the three cases are, in both instances, mutually exclusive and exhaust all possibilities.

Theorem 155: $(X + Y)^* = X^* + Y^*;$

$$(X - Y)^* = X^* - Y^*, \quad \text{if } X > Y;$$

$$(XY)^* = X^* Y^*;$$

$$\left(\frac{X}{Y}\right)^* = \frac{X^*}{Y^*}.$$

Proof: I) a) Every lower number for $X^* + Y^*$ is the sum of a rational number $< X$ and of a rational number $< Y$; it is therefore $< X + Y$, and is thus a lower number for $(X + Y)^*$.

𝔟) Every lower number U for $(X + Y)^*$ is $< X + Y$. Now

$$\frac{U}{X+Y} < 1,$$

$$U = X \frac{U}{X+Y} + Y \frac{U}{X+Y}$$

implies that U, as the sum of a rational number $< X$ and of a rational number $< Y$, is a lower number for $X^* + Y^*$.

Hence we have

$$(X+Y)^* = X^* + Y^*.$$

II) If

$$X > Y$$

then

$$X = (X - Y) + Y,$$

so that by 1),

$$X^* = (X - Y)^* + Y^*,$$

$$(X - Y)^* = X^* - Y^*.$$

III) 𝔞) Every lower number for $X^* Y^*$ is the product of a rational number $< X$ and of a rational number $< Y$; therefore it is $< XY$, and so is a lower number for $(XY)^*$.

𝔟) Every lower number U for $(XY)^*$ is $< XY$. Choose a rational number U_1, by Theorem 91, such that

$$U < U_1 < XY$$

Then

$$\frac{U}{U_1} < 1$$

and

$$\frac{U_1}{Y} < X.$$

Thus the relation

$$U = \frac{U_1}{Y}\left(Y \frac{U}{U_1}\right)$$

represents U as the product of a lower number for X^* and a lower number for Y^*. Therefore U is a lower number for $X^* Y^*$.

Hence we have

$$(XY)^* = X^* Y^*.$$

IV) $$X = \frac{X}{Y} Y,$$

so that by III), we obtain

$$X^* = \left(\frac{X}{Y}\right)^* Y^*,$$

$$\left(\frac{X}{Y}\right)^* = \frac{X^*}{Y^*}.$$

Theorem 156: *The integral cuts satisfy the five axioms of the natural numbers if the role of* 1 *is assigned to* 1^* *and if we set*

$$(x^*)' = (x')^*.$$

Proof: Let $\mathfrak{Z}^*$ be the set of all integral cuts.

1) 1^* belongs to $\mathfrak{Z}^*$.

2) For every x^* in $\mathfrak{Z}^*$, the cut $(x^*)'$ is also in $\mathfrak{Z}^*$.

3) We always have

$$x' \neq 1,$$

hence

$$(x')^* \neq 1^*,$$
$$(x^*)' \neq 1^*.$$

4) If

$$(x^*)' = (y^*)'$$

then

$$(x')^* = (y')^*,$$
$$x' = y',$$
$$x = y,$$
$$x^* = y^*.$$

5) Let a set $\mathfrak{M}^*$ of integral cuts have the following properties:

I) 1^* belongs to $\mathfrak{M}^*$.

II) If x^* belongs to $\mathfrak{M}^*$, then so does $(x^*)'$.

Also, denote by $\mathfrak{M}$ the set of x for which x^* belongs to $\mathfrak{M}^*$. Then 1 belongs to $\mathfrak{M}$, and if x belongs to $\mathfrak{M}$ then so does x'. Hence every integer belongs to $\mathfrak{M}$, so that every integral cut belongs to $\mathfrak{M}^*$.

Since $=$, $>$, $<$, sum, difference (whenever it exists), product, and quotient, in the domain of rational cuts all correspond to the earlier concepts (by Theorems 154 and 155), the rational cuts have all the properties which we have proved, in Chapter 2, attach to the rational numbers; the integral cuts, in particular, have all the properties that have been established for the integers.

Therefore, we throw out the rational numbers and replace them by the corresponding rational cuts, so that in all that follows we will only have to speak in terms of cuts whenever any of the foregoing material is involved. (However, the rational numbers survive—in sets—in the concept of cut.)

Definition 41: *The symbol* X (now freed of its previous meaning) *will denote the rational cut* X^* *to which we also transfer the name "rational number"; the name "integer" will similarly be transferred, to apply to integral cuts.*

Thus, for instance, we will simply write

$$\xi \frac{1}{\xi} = 1$$

instead of

$$\xi \frac{1^*}{\xi} = 1^*.$$

Theorem 157: *The rational numbers are those cuts for which there exists a least upper number* X. *This* X *is then the cut.*

Proof: 1) For the cut X (our old X^*), X (the rational number in the old sense) is a least upper number.

2) If there exists a least upper number X for a cut ξ, then every lower number for ξ is $< X$ and every upper number is $\geqq X$, so that the cut is X (the old X^*).

Theorem 158: *Let* ξ *be a cut. Then* X *is a lower number if, and only if,*

$$X < \xi,$$

and hence is an upper number if, and only if,

$$X \geqq \xi.$$

Proof: 1) If X is a lower number for ξ, then, noting that X is an upper number for X (the old X^*), we have

$$X < \xi.$$

2) If X is an upper number for ξ, and is the least such, then we have by Theorem 157 that

$$X = \xi.$$

3) If X is an upper number for ξ but is not the least such, we choose an upper number X_1 less than X. Then X_1 is a lower number for X, so that

$$X > \xi.$$

Theorem 159: *If*

$$\xi < \eta,$$

then there exists a Z *such that*

$$\xi < Z < \eta.$$

Proof: Choose an upper number X for ξ which is a lower number for η, and then choose a greater lower number Z for η. Then we have by Theorem 158 that

$$\xi \leqq X < Z < \eta.$$

Theorem 160: *Every*

$$Z > \xi\eta$$

may be brought into the form

$$Z = XY,\ X \geqq \xi,\ Y \geqq \eta.$$

Proof: Denote by ζ the lesser of the two cuts 1 and $\dfrac{Z-\xi\eta}{(\xi+\eta)+1}$.

Then

$$\zeta \leqq 1,\ \zeta \leqq \frac{Z-\xi\eta}{(\xi+\eta)+1}.$$

Choose Z_1 and Z_2 by Theorem 159 such that

$$\xi < Z_1 < \xi+\zeta,\ \eta < Z_2 < \eta+\zeta.$$

Then we have

$$Z_1 Z_2 < (\xi+\zeta)(\eta+\zeta) = (\xi+\zeta)\eta+(\xi+\zeta)\zeta \leqq (\xi+\zeta)\eta+(\xi+1)\zeta$$
$$= (\xi\eta+\eta\zeta)+(\xi+1)\zeta = \xi\eta+((\xi+\eta)+1)\zeta \leqq \xi\eta+(Z-\xi\eta) = Z.$$

By means of

$$Z = \frac{Z}{Z_2} Z_2$$

and using

$$X = \frac{Z}{Z_2} = Z\frac{1}{Z_2} > (Z_1 Z_2)\frac{1}{Z_2} = Z_1 > \xi,$$
$$Y = Z_2 > \eta,$$

we have decomposed Z as required.

Theorem 161: *For each* ζ, *the equation*

$$\xi\xi = \zeta$$

has exactly one solution.

Proof: I) There exists at most one solution; for if

$$\xi_1 > \xi_2$$

then

$$\xi_1 \xi_1 > \xi_2 \xi_2.$$

II) Consider the set of all rational numbers X for which

$$XX < \zeta.$$

This set constitutes a cut, for:

1) If

$$X < 1 \text{ and } X < \zeta,$$

then

$$XX < X \cdot 1 = X < \zeta.$$

If

$$X \geqq 1 \text{ and } X \geqq \zeta,$$

then

$$XX \geqq X \cdot 1 = X \geqq \zeta.$$

2) If

$$XX < \zeta,\ Y < X$$

then

$$YY < XX < \zeta.$$

3) Let

$$XX < \zeta.$$

Choose a Z less than the lesser of the two cuts 1 and $\frac{\zeta - XX}{X + (X+1)}$.
Then

$$Z < 1,\ Z < \frac{\zeta - XX}{X + (X+1)};$$

furthermore, we have

$$X + Z > X$$

and

$$(X+Z)(X+Z) = (X+Z)X + (X+Z)Z < (XX + ZX) + (X+1)Z$$
$$= XX + (X + (X+1))Z < XX + (\zeta - XX) = \zeta.$$

If we denote by ξ the cut which we have constructed, then we now assert that

$$\xi\xi = \zeta.$$

If we had

$$\xi\xi > \zeta,$$

then we could choose, by Theorem 159, a Z such that

$$\xi\xi > Z > \zeta.$$

This Z, being a lower number for $\xi\xi$, would satisfy

$$Z = X_1 X_2,\ X_1 < \xi,\ X_2 < \xi;$$

if X denotes the greater of the two numbers X_1 and X_2, then we would have, in contradiction to the above, that

$$X < \xi,$$
$$Z \leqq XX < \zeta.$$

If we had

$$\xi\xi < \zeta,$$

then we could choose, by Theorem 159, a Z such that

$$\xi\xi < Z < \zeta.$$

By Theorem 160, Z would be of the form

$$Z = X_1 X_2, \ X_1 \geqq \xi, \ X_2 \geqq \xi;$$

if X denotes the lesser of the two numbers X_1 and X_2, then we would have, in contradiction to the above, that

$$X \geqq \xi,$$
$$Z \geqq XX \geqq \zeta.$$

Definition 42: *Any cut which is not a rational number is called an irrational number.*

Theorem 162: *There exists an irrational number.*

Proof: It suffices to show that the solution of

$$\xi\xi = 1',$$

whose existence is guaranteed by Theorem 161, is irrational.

Otherwise, we would have

$$\xi = \frac{x}{y};$$

among all such representations we choose one, by Theorem 27, for which y is as small as possible. Since

$$1' = \xi\xi = \frac{x}{y} \cdot \frac{x}{y} = \frac{xx}{yy},$$

we have

$$yy < 1'(yy) = xx = (1'y)y < (1'y)(1'y),$$
$$y < x < 1'y.$$

Set

$$x - y = u.$$

Then

$$y + u = x < 1'y = y + y,$$
$$u < y.$$

Now we have that

$$(v+w)(v+w) = (v+w)v + (v+w)w = (vv+wv) + (vw+ww)$$
$$= (vv + 1'(vw)) + ww,$$

hence, setting

$$y - u = t$$

that

$$\begin{aligned} xx + tt &= (y+u)(y+u) + tt = (yy + 1'(yu)) + (uu + tt) \\ &= (yy + (1'u)(u+t)) + (uu + tt) \\ &= (yy + 1'(uu)) + ((1'(ut) + uu) + tt) \\ &= (yy + 1'(uu)) + (u+t)(u+t) \\ &= (yy + 1'(uu)) + yy = 1'(yy) + 1'(uu) = xx + 1'(uu), \end{aligned}$$

$$tt = 1'(uu),$$

$$\frac{t}{u} \cdot \frac{t}{u} = 1',$$

which contradicts

$$u < y.$$

CHAPTER IV

REAL NUMBERS

§ 1

Definition

Definition 43: *The cuts will henceforth be called "positive numbers"; similarly, what we have been calling "rational numbers" and "integers" will henceforth be called "positive rational numbers" and "positive integers," respectively.*

We create a new number 0 (to be read "zero"), *distinct from the positive numbers.*

We also create numbers which are distinct from the positive numbers as well as distinct from zero, and which we will call negative numbers, in such a way that to each ξ (i.e. to each positive number) *we assign a negative number denoted by* $-\xi$ ($-$ to be read "minus"). *In this,* $-\xi$ *and* $-\eta$ *will be considered as the same number (as equal) if and only if* ξ *and* η *are the same number.*

The totality consisting of all positive numbers, of 0, *and of all negative numbers, will be called the real numbers.*

Capital Greek letters (such as Ξ, H, Z, Y) will be used throughout to denote real numbers, except where otherwise specified. "Equal" will be written "$=$" and "unequal" ("different") as "$\neq$".

Thus for any given Ξ and H, exactly one of

$$\Xi = H,\quad \Xi \neq H$$

is the case. For real numbers, the concepts of identity and of equality are merged, so that the following three theorems are trivial:

Theorem 163:

$$\Xi = \Xi.$$

Theorem 164: *If*

$$\Xi = H$$

then

$$H = \Xi.$$

Theorem 165: *If*

$$\Xi = H,\quad H = Z$$

then

$$\Xi = Z.$$

§ 2

Ordering

Definition 44:

$$|\Xi| = \begin{cases} \xi & \text{if} \quad \Xi = \xi, \\ 0 & \text{if} \quad \Xi = 0, \\ \xi & \text{if} \quad \Xi = -\xi. \end{cases}$$

The number $|\Xi|$ *is called the absolute value of* Ξ.

Theorem 166: $|\Xi|$ *is positive, for positive and for negative* Ξ.

Proof: Definition 44.

Definition 45: *If* Ξ *and* H *are not both positive, then*

$$\Xi > H$$

if and only if we have

either Ξ *negative,* H *negative and* $|\Xi| < |H|$,
or $\Xi = 0$, H *negative,*
or Ξ *positive,* H *negative,*
or Ξ *positive,* $H = 0$.

($>$ to be read "is greater than.")

Note that, in case Ξ and H are positive, we already have the concepts "$>$" and "$<$"; the latter, in fact, has been used in one of the cases of Definition 45.

Definition 46: $\Xi < H$

means $H > \Xi$.

($<$ to be read "is less than.")

Note that if Ξ and H are positive, Definition 46 is in agreement with our old concepts.

Theorem 167: *For any given* Ξ *and* H, *exactly one of*

$$\Xi = H, \; \Xi > H, \; \Xi < H$$

is the case.

Proof: 1) For positive Ξ and H we know this from Theorem 123.

2) If Ξ is positive while H is $= 0$ or negative, then

$$\Xi \neq H,$$

and furthermore, by Definition 45,

$$\Xi > H,$$

and finally, by Definition 46,

$$\Xi \text{ not } < H.$$

3) If $\Xi = 0$ while H is positive, then

$$\Xi \neq H,$$

and furthermore, by Definition 45,

$$\Xi \text{ not } > H,$$

and finally, by Definition 46,

$$\Xi < H.$$

4) If $\Xi = 0$, $H = 0$, then

$$\Xi = H,$$
$$\Xi \text{ not } > H,$$
$$\Xi \text{ not } < H.$$

5) If $\Xi = 0$ while H is negative, then

$$\Xi \neq H,$$
$$\Xi > H,$$
$$\Xi \text{ not } < H.$$

6) If Ξ is negative while H is positive or $= 0$, then

$$\Xi \neq H,$$
$$\Xi \text{ not } > H,$$
$$\Xi < H.$$

7) If Ξ and H are both negative, then

$$\Xi \neq H,\quad \Xi > H,\quad \Xi \text{ not } < H \text{ for } |\Xi| < |H|,$$
$$\Xi = H,\quad \Xi \text{ not } > H,\quad \Xi \text{ not } < H \text{ for } |\Xi| = |H|,$$
$$\Xi \neq H,\quad \Xi \text{ not } > H,\quad \Xi < H \text{ for } |\Xi| > |H|.$$

Definition 47: $\Xi \geqq H$

means

$$\Xi > H \text{ or } \Xi = H.$$

($\geqq$ to be read "is greater than or equal to.")

Definition 48: $\Xi \leqq H$

means

$$\Xi < H \text{ or } \Xi = H.$$

($\leqq$ to be read "is less than or equal to.")

Theorem 168: *If*

$$\Xi \geqq H$$

then

$$H \leqq \Xi$$

and vice versa.

Proof: Definition 46.

Theorem 169: *The positive numbers are the numbers which are > 0; the negative numbers are the numbers which are < 0.*

Proof: 1) By Definition 45, we have

$$\xi > 0.$$

2) If

$$\Xi > 0$$

then, by Definition 45,

$$\Xi = \xi.$$

3) By Definition 46, we have

$$-\xi < 0.$$

4) If

$$\Xi < 0$$

then, by Definition 46,

$$\Xi = -\xi.$$

Theorem 170:

$$|\Xi| \geqq 0.$$

Proof: Definition 44, Theorem 166, and Theorem 169.

Theorem 171 (Transitivity of Ordering): *If*

$$\Xi < H, \quad H < Z$$

then

$$\Xi < Z.$$

Proof: 1) Let

$$Z > 0,$$

If

$$\Xi > 0,$$

then

$$H > 0,$$

and we have the earlier Theorem 126.

If

$$\Xi \leqq 0,$$

then certainly

$$\Xi < Z.$$

2) Let

$$Z = 0.$$

then

$$H < 0,$$

hence

$$\Xi < 0,$$
$$\Xi < Z.$$

3) Let

$$Z < 0,$$

then

$$H < 0,$$
$$\Xi < 0.$$

We also have

$$|\Xi| > |H|, \ |H| > |Z|,$$

hence

$$|\Xi| > |Z|,$$
$$\Xi < Z.$$

Theorem 172: *If*

$$\Xi \leqq H, \ H < Z \ \text{or} \ \Xi < H, \ H \leqq Z$$

then

$$\Xi < Z.$$

Proof: Obvious if an equality sign holds in the hypothesis; otherwise, Theorem 171 does it.

Theorem 173: *If* $\Xi \leqq H, \ H \leqq Z,$

then

$$\Xi \leqq Z.$$

Proof: Obvious if two equality signs hold in the hypothesis; otherwise, Theorem 172 does it.

Definition 49: *If* $\Xi \leqq 0$

then Ξ is called rational if either

$$\Xi = 0$$

or

$$\Xi < 0, \ |\Xi| \ \text{a rational number.}$$

Thus we now have positive rational numbers, the rational number 0, and negative rational numbers.

Definition 50: *If*

$$\Xi < 0$$

then Ξ is called irrational in case it is not rational.

Thus we now have positive irrational numbers and negative irrational numbers. (Numbers? Yes; for, we had an irrational ξ, and the positive number $\xi + X$ is always irrational, since

$$\xi + X = Y$$

would imply

$$\xi = Y - X;$$

similarly, $-(\xi + X)$ is always negative irrational.)

Definition 51: *If*

$$\Xi \leqq 0$$

then Ξ is called integral (or an integer) if either

$$\Xi = 0$$

or

$$\Xi < 0, \ |\Xi| \ \text{an integer.}$$

Thus we now have positive integers, the integer 0, and negative integers.

Theorem 174: *Every integer is rational.*

Proof: We already know this in the case of positive numbers. For 0 and for negative numbers, it follows from Definitions 49 and 51.

§ 3

Addition

Definition 52:

$$\Xi + H = \begin{cases} -(|\Xi| + |H|) & \text{if } \Xi < 0,\ H < 0; \\ \left.\begin{array}{c} |\Xi| - |H| \\ 0 \\ -(|H| - |\Xi|) \end{array}\right\} & \text{if } \Xi > 0,\ H < 0, \left\{\begin{array}{l} |\Xi| > |H|; \\ |\Xi| = |H|; \\ |\Xi| < |H|; \end{array}\right. \\ H + \Xi & \text{if } \Xi < 0,\ H > 0; \\ H & \text{if } \Xi = 0; \\ \Xi & \text{if } H = 0. \end{cases}$$

(+ to be read "plus.") *$\Xi + H$ is called the sum of Ξ and H, or the number obtained by addition of H to Ξ.*

In this definition, note the following:

1) For

$$\Xi > 0,\ H > 0$$

we had the concept of $\Xi + H$ as early as Definition 34.

2) This same concept is used in Definition 52.

3) The third case of Definition 52 uses the concept of sum as introduced in the second case.

4) The fourth case and the fifth case overlap for

$$\Xi = H = 0;$$

but the number defined as $\Xi + H$ is the same (namely 0) in the two cases.

Theorem 175 (Commutative Law of Addition):

$$\Xi + H = H + \Xi.$$

Proof: If

$$\Xi = 0,$$

then each side reduces to H; if

$$H = 0,$$

then each side $= \Xi$.

If

$$\Xi > 0,\ H > 0,$$

then Theorem 175 is the earlier Theorem 130.

If
$$\Xi < 0,\ H < 0$$
then, by Theorem 130,
$$\Xi + H = -(|\Xi| + |H|) = -(|H| + |\Xi|) = H + \Xi.$$
If
$$\Xi < 0,\ H > 0$$
then the assertion reduces to the definition itself.

If
$$\Xi > 0,\ H < 0$$
then we have by the preceding case that
$$H + \Xi = \Xi + H,$$
hence
$$\Xi + H = H + \Xi.$$

Definition 53: $$-\Xi = \begin{cases} 0 & \textit{for } \Xi = 0, \\ |\Xi| & \textit{for } \Xi < 0. \end{cases}$$

(— to be read "minus.")

Note that for $\Xi > 0$, we have the concept $-\Xi$ from Definition 43.

Theorem 176: *If*
$$\Xi > 0,\ \textit{or}\ \Xi = 0,\ \textit{or}\ \Xi < 0,$$
then
$$-\Xi < 0,\ \textit{or}\ -\Xi = 0,\ \textit{or}\ -\Xi > 0,\ \textit{respectively,}$$
and vice versa.

Proof: Definition 43 and Definition 53.

Theorem 177: $$-(-\Xi) = \Xi.$$

Proof: Definitions 43, 44, and 53.

Theorem 178: $$|-\Xi| = |\Xi|.$$

Proof: Definitions 43, 44, and 53.

Theorem 179: $$\Xi + (-\Xi) = 0.$$

Proof: Definition 52, Definition 53, and Theorem 178.

Theorem 180: $$-(\Xi + H) = -\Xi + (-H).$$

Proof: By Theorem 175, we have
$$-(\Xi + H) = -(H + \Xi)$$
and
$$-\Xi + (-H) = -H + (-\Xi);$$
hence without loss of generality, we may assume that
$$\Xi \geqq H;$$

for, at least one of the relations

$$\Xi \geqq H,\ H \geqq \Xi$$

holds, and

$$-(H+\Xi) = -H+(-\Xi)$$

implies

$$-(\Xi+H) = -\Xi+(-H).$$

Thus let

$$\Xi \geqq H.$$

1) If

$$\Xi > 0,\ H > 0,$$

then

$$-\Xi+(-H) = -(\Xi+H).$$

2) If

$$\Xi > 0,\ H = 0,$$

then

$$-\Xi+(-H) = -\Xi+0 = -\Xi = -(\Xi+0) = -(\Xi+H).$$

3) If

$$\Xi > 0,\ H < 0,$$

then

either

$$\Xi > |H|,$$

hence

$$\Xi+H = \Xi-|H|,$$

$$-\Xi+(-H) = -\Xi+|H| = -(\Xi-|H|) = -(\Xi+H);$$

or

$$\Xi = |H|,$$

hence

$$\Xi+H = 0,$$

$$-\Xi+(-H) = -\Xi+|H| = 0 = -(\Xi+H);$$

or

$$\Xi < |H|,$$

hence

$$\Xi+H = -(|H|-\Xi),$$

$$-\Xi+(-H) = -\Xi+|H| = |H|-\Xi = -(\Xi+H).$$

4) If

$$\Xi = 0,$$

then

$$-\Xi+(-H) = 0+(-H) = -H = -(0+H) = -(\Xi+H).$$

5) If

$$\Xi < 0,$$

then

$$H < 0,$$

$$\Xi+H = -(|\Xi|+|H|),$$

$$-\Xi+(-H) = |\Xi|+|H| = -(\Xi+H).$$

Definition 54: $\Xi - H = \Xi + (-H)$.

(— to be read "minus.") *$\Xi - H$ is called the difference Ξ minus H, or the number obtained by subtraction of H from Ξ.*

Note that Definition 54 agrees (as it should), for the case

$$\Xi > H > 0,$$

with the earlier Definition 35; for in this case, we have that

$$\Xi > 0, \ -H < 0, \ |\Xi| > |-H|, \ \Xi + (-H) = |\Xi| - |-H| = \Xi - H.$$

Theorem 181: $-(\Xi - H) = H - \Xi.$

Proof: By Theorems 180 and 177, we have

$$-(\Xi - H) = -(\Xi + (-H)) = -\Xi + (-(-H)) = -\Xi + H = H + (-\Xi)$$
$$= H - \Xi.$$

Theorem 182: *If*

$$\Xi - H > 0, \ \textit{or} \ \Xi - H = 0, \ \textit{or} \ \Xi - H < 0,$$

then

$$\Xi > H, \ \textit{or} \ \Xi = H, \ \textit{or} \ \Xi < H, \ \textit{respectively,}$$

and vice versa.

Proof: Since $-H$ (as well as H itself) stands for any real number at all, we may write $-H$ in place of H, and we must then show that the cases

$$\Xi + H > 0, \text{or } \Xi + H = 0, \text{ or } \Xi + H < 0,$$

correspond to the cases

$$\Xi > -H, \text{ or } \Xi = -H, \text{ or } \Xi < -H,$$

respectively.

Indeed, the assertion is obvious if $\Xi = 0$ or $H = 0$. As for the rest, if we have the case

$$\Xi > 0, \ H > 0,$$

or any of the first three cases of Definition 52, we need only verify — decomposing the third case into the three subordinate cases

$$|H| > |\Xi|, \ |H| = |\Xi|, \ |H| < |\Xi|$$

— that we obtain the signs

$$>, =, <, >, =, <, >, =, <, \text{ respectively,}$$

simultaneously in both of the above instances.

Theorem 183: *If*

$$\Xi > H, \ \textit{or} \ \Xi = H, \ \textit{or} \ \Xi < H,$$

then

$$-\Xi < -H, \text{ or } -\Xi = -H, \text{ or } -\Xi > -H, \textit{ respectively,}$$

and vice versa.

Proof: By Theorem 182, the former corresponds to the cases

$$\Xi - H > 0 \text{ , or } \Xi - H = 0 \text{ , or } \Xi - H < 0,$$

respectively, and the latter to the cases

$$-H - (-\Xi) > 0 \text{ , or } -H - (-\Xi) = 0 \text{ , or } -H - (-\Xi) < 0,$$

respectively, so that the relations

$$-H - (-\Xi) = -H + (-(-\Xi)) = -H + \Xi = \Xi + (-H) = \Xi - H$$

prove everything.

Theorem 184: *Every real number can be represented as the difference of two positive numbers.*

Proof: 1) If

$$\Xi > 0,$$

then

$$\Xi = (\Xi + 1) - 1.$$

2) If

$$\Xi = 0,$$

then

$$\Xi = 1 - 1.$$

3) If

$$\Xi < 0,$$

then

$$-\Xi = |\Xi| = (|\Xi| + 1) - 1,$$

$$\Xi = -((|\Xi| + 1) - 1) = 1 - (|\Xi| + 1).$$

Theorem 185: *If*

$$\Xi = \xi_1 - \xi_2, \quad H = \eta_1 - \eta_2$$

then

$$\Xi + H = (\xi_1 + \eta_1) - (\xi_2 + \eta_2).$$

Proof: 1) Let

$$\Xi > 0, \; H > 0.$$

Then, since

$$(\alpha + \beta) + (\gamma + \delta) = (\alpha + \beta) + (\delta + \gamma) = ((\alpha + \beta) + \delta) + \gamma$$
$$= \gamma + (\alpha + (\beta + \delta)) = (\gamma + \alpha) + (\beta + \delta),$$

we have

$$(\Xi + H) + (\xi_2 + \eta_2) = \xi_1 + \eta_1,$$

so that the assertion is true.

2) Let

$$\Xi < 0, \quad H < 0.$$

Then, by Theorem 181,

$$\xi_2 - \xi_1 = -\Xi > 0, \quad \eta_2 - \eta_1 = -H > 0,$$

so that 1) yields

$$-\Xi + (-H) = (\xi_2 + \eta_2) - (\xi_1 + \eta_1),$$
$$\Xi + H = -(-\Xi + (-H)) = (\xi_1 + \eta_1) - (\xi_2 + \eta_2).$$

3) Let

$$\Xi > 0, \quad H < 0,$$

hence

$$\xi_1 - \xi_2 > 0, \quad \eta_2 - \eta_1 > 0.$$

A) If

$$\Xi > |H|,$$

then

$$\xi_1 - \xi_2 > \eta_2 - \eta_1,$$

so that

$$\begin{aligned}
\xi_1 + \eta_1 &= ((\xi_1 - \xi_2) + \xi_2) + \eta_1 = (\xi_1 - \xi_2) + (\xi_2 + \eta_1) = (\xi_2 + \eta_1) + (\xi_1 - \xi_2)\\
&= (\xi_2 + \eta_1) + ((\eta_2 - \eta_1) + ((\xi_1 - \xi_2) - (\eta_2 - \eta_1)))\\
&= ((\xi_2 + \eta_1) + (\eta_2 - \eta_1)) + ((\xi_1 - \xi_2) - (\eta_2 - \eta_1))\\
&= (\xi_2 + (\eta_1 + (\eta_2 - \eta_1))) + ((\xi_1 - \xi_2) - (\eta_2 - \eta_1))\\
&= (\xi_2 + \eta_2) + ((\xi_1 - \xi_2) - (\eta_2 - \eta_1)),
\end{aligned}$$

$$(\xi_1 + \eta_1) - (\xi_2 + \eta_2) = (\xi_1 - \xi_2) - (\eta_2 - \eta_1) = \Xi - |H| = \Xi + H.$$

B) If

$$\Xi < |H|,$$

then A) yields

$$\begin{aligned}
\Xi + H &= -(-H + (-\Xi)) = -((\eta_2 - \eta_1) + (\xi_2 - \xi_1))\\
&= -((\eta_2 + \xi_2) - (\eta_1 + \xi_1)) = (\eta_1 + \xi_1) - (\eta_2 + \xi_2)\\
&= (\xi_1 + \eta_1) - (\xi_2 + \eta_2).
\end{aligned}$$

C) If

$$\Xi = |H|,$$

hence

$$\xi_1 - \xi_2 = \eta_2 - \eta_1,$$

then

$$\xi_1 = \xi_2 + (\eta_2 - \eta_1),$$
$$\xi_1 + \eta_1 = \xi_2 + \eta_2,$$
$$\Xi + H = 0 = (\xi_1 + \eta_1) - (\xi_2 + \eta_2).$$

4) Let

$$\Xi < 0, \quad H > 0.$$

Then 3) yields

$$H+\Xi = (\eta_1+\xi_1)-(\eta_2+\xi_2),$$
$$\Xi+H = (\xi_1+\eta_1)-(\xi_2+\eta_2).$$

5) Let

$$\Xi = 0.$$

Then

$$\xi_1 = \xi_2,$$
$$\Xi+H = H.$$

a) If

$$\eta_1 > \eta_2$$

then

$$(\eta_1-\eta_2)+(\xi_1+\eta_2) = ((\eta_1-\eta_2)+\eta_2)+\xi_1 = \eta_1+\xi_1 = \xi_1+\eta_1,$$
$$H = \eta_1-\eta_2 = (\xi_1+\eta_1)-(\xi_1+\eta_2) = (\xi_1+\eta_1)-(\xi_2+\eta_2).$$

b) If

$$\eta_1 = \eta_2$$

then

$$H = 0 = (\xi_1+\eta_1)-(\xi_2+\eta_2).$$

c) If

$$\eta_1 < \eta_2$$

then, by a),

$$-H = \eta_2-\eta_1 = (\xi_2+\eta_2)-(\xi_1+\eta_1),$$
$$H = -(-H) = (\xi_1+\eta_1)-(\xi_2+\eta_2).$$

6) Let

$$H = 0.$$

Then, by 5),

$$\Xi+H = H+\Xi = (\eta_1+\xi_1)-(\eta_2+\xi_2) = (\xi_1+\eta_1)-(\xi_2+\eta_2).$$

Theorem 186 (Associative Law of Addition):

$$(\Xi+H)+Z = \Xi+(H+Z).$$

Proof: By Theorem 184, we have that

$$\Xi = \xi_1-\xi_2, \quad H = \eta_1-\eta_2, \quad Z = \zeta_1-\zeta_2.$$

Now Theorem 185 yields

$$(\Xi+H)+Z = ((\xi_1+\eta_1)-(\xi_2+\eta_2))+(\zeta_1-\zeta_2)$$
$$= ((\xi_1+\eta_1)+\zeta_1)-((\xi_2+\eta_2)+\zeta_2) = (\xi_1+(\eta_1+\zeta_1))-(\xi_2+(\eta_2+\zeta_2))$$
$$= (\xi_1-\xi_2)+((\eta_1+\zeta_1)-(\eta_2+\zeta_2)) = \Xi+(H+Z).$$

Theorem 187: *For any given Ξ, H, the equation*

$$H+Y = \Xi$$

has exactly one solution Y, namely

$$Y = \Xi - H.$$

Proof: 1)
$$Y = \Xi - H$$
is a solution, since by Theorem 186 we have

$$H + (\Xi - H) = (\Xi - H) + H = (\Xi + (-H)) + H = \Xi + (-H + H)$$
$$= \Xi + 0 = \Xi.$$

2) If
$$H + Y = \Xi$$
then
$$\Xi - H = \Xi + (-H) = -H + \Xi = -H + (H + Y) = (-H + H) + Y$$
$$= 0 + Y = Y.$$

Theorem 188: *We have*

$$\Xi + Z > H + Z, \text{ or } \Xi + Z = H + Z, \text{ or } \Xi + Z < H + Z,$$

respectively, according to whether

$$\Xi > H, \text{ or } \Xi = H, \text{ or } \Xi < H.$$

Proof: By Theorem 182, the former relations hold according to whether

$$(\Xi + Z) - (H + Z) > 0, \text{ or } (\Xi + Z) - (H + Z) = 0,$$
$$\text{or } (\Xi + Z) - (H + Z) < 0,$$

respectively, and the latter according to whether

$$\Xi - H > 0, \text{ or } \Xi - H = 0, \text{ or } \Xi - H < 0.$$

The relations

$$(\Xi + Z) - (H + Z) = (\Xi + Z) + (-Z + (-H)) = (\Xi + (Z + (-Z))) + (-H)$$
$$= \Xi + (-H) = \Xi - H$$

then prove the assertions of the theorem.

Theorem 189: *If*

$$\Xi > H, \ Z > Y$$

then

$$\Xi + Z > H + Y.$$

Proof: By Theorem 188, we have
$$\Xi + Z > H + Z$$
and
$$H + Z = Z + H > Y + H = H + Y,$$
so that
$$\Xi + Z > H + Y.$$

Theorem 190: *If*

$$\Xi \geqq H,\ Z > Y \quad or \quad \Xi > H,\ Z \geqq Y$$

then

$$\Xi + Z > H + Y.$$

Proof: Follows from Theorem 188 if an equality sign holds in the hypothesis; otherwise, from Theorem 189.

Theorem 191: *If*

$$\Xi \geqq H,\ Z \geqq Y,$$

then

$$\Xi + Z \geqq H + Y.$$

Proof: Obvious if two equality signs hold in the hypothesis; otherwise, Theorem 190 does it.

§ 4

Multiplication

Definition 55:

$$\Xi \cdot H = \begin{cases} -(|\Xi||H|), & \text{if } \Xi > 0,\ H < 0 \text{ or } \Xi < 0,\ H > 0; \\ |\Xi||H|, & \text{if } \Xi < 0,\ H < 0; \\ 0, & \text{if } \Xi = 0 \text{ or } H = 0. \end{cases}$$

($\cdot$ to be read "times"; however, the dot is usually omitted.) $\Xi \cdot H$ *is called the product of* Ξ *by* H, *or the number obtained from multiplication of* Ξ *by* H.

Note that the product $\Xi \cdot H$ for the case $\Xi > 0$, $H > 0$ was defined earlier (cf. Definition 36), a fact used in Definition 55.

Theorem 192: *We have*

$$\Xi H = 0$$

if, and only if, at least one of the two numbers Ξ, H *is zero.*

Proof: Definition 55.

Theorem 193: $$|\Xi H| = |\Xi||H|.$$

Proof: Definition 55.

Theorem 194 (Commutative Law of Multiplication):

$$\Xi H = H \Xi.$$

Proof: If $\Xi > 0$, $H > 0$, this is Theorem 142; in the other cases, it follows from Definition 55, since the right-hand side of Definition 55 is symmetric in Ξ, H (by Theorem 142), as is also its subdivision into cases.

Theorem 195: $$\Xi \cdot 1 = \Xi.$$

Proof: For $\Xi > 0$, this follows from Theorem 151; for $\Xi = 0$, from Definition 55; for $\Xi < 0$ we have, by Definition 55, that

$$\Xi \cdot 1 = -(|\Xi| \cdot 1) = -|\Xi| = \Xi.$$

Theorem 196: *If*

$$\Xi \neq 0, \quad H \neq 0,$$

then

$$\Xi H = |\Xi||H| \quad \text{or} \quad \Xi H = -(|\Xi||H|),$$

where the first alternative holds if none or both of the numbers Ξ, H *are negative, and the second if exactly one of these numbers is negative.*

Proof: Definition 55.

Theorem 197: $(-\Xi)H = \Xi(-H) = -(\Xi H)$.

Proof: 1) If one of the numbers Ξ, H is zero, then all three of the expressions are 0.

2) If

$$\Xi \neq 0, \ H \neq 0,$$

then by Theorem 193, all three of the expressions have the same absolute value $|\Xi|\cdot|H|$, and all three will, by Theorem 196, be > 0 or < 0 according to whether or not exactly one of the numbers Ξ, H is negative.

Theorem 198: $(-\Xi)(-H) = \Xi H.$

Proof: By Theorem 197, we have

$$(-\Xi)(-H) = \Xi(-(-H)) = \Xi H.$$

Theorem 199 (Associative Law of Multiplication):

$$(\Xi H)\mathrm{Z} = \Xi(H\mathrm{Z}).$$

Proof: 1) If one of the numbers Ξ, H, Z is zero, then both sides are 0.

2) If

$$\Xi \neq 0, \ H \neq 0, \ \mathrm{Z} \neq 0,$$

then by Theorem 193, both sides have the same absolute value

$$(|\Xi||H|)|\mathrm{Z}| = |\Xi|(|H||\mathrm{Z}|),$$

and by Theorem 196, both sides are > 0 if none or two of the numbers Ξ, H, Z are negative, while both sides are < 0 if exactly one or all three of those numbers are negative.

Theorem 200: $\xi(\eta-\zeta) = \xi\eta - \xi\zeta.$

Proof: 1) If

$$\eta > \zeta$$

then

$$(\eta-\zeta)+\zeta = \eta,$$

so that, by Theorem 144,

$$\xi(\eta-\zeta)+\xi\zeta = \xi\eta,$$

$$\xi(\eta-\zeta) = \xi\eta - \xi\zeta.$$

2) If

$$\eta = \zeta$$

then

$$\xi\eta = \xi\zeta,$$

$$\xi(\eta-\zeta) = \xi\cdot 0 = 0 = \xi\eta - \xi\zeta.$$

3) If

$$\eta < \zeta$$

then we have by 1) that

$$\xi(\zeta - \eta) = \xi\zeta - \xi\eta,$$

$$\xi(\eta - \zeta) = \xi(-(\zeta - \eta)) = -(\xi(\zeta - \eta)) = -(\xi\zeta - \xi\eta) = \xi\eta - \xi\zeta.$$

Theorem 201 (Distributive Law):

$$\Xi(H + Z) = \Xi H + \Xi Z.$$

Proof: 1) Let

$$\Xi > 0.$$

By Theorem 184, we have

$$H = \eta_1 - \eta_2, \quad Z = \zeta_1 - \zeta_2,$$

hence, by Theorem 185,

$$H + Z = (\eta_1 + \zeta_1) - (\eta_2 + \zeta_2),$$

so that, by Theorems 200 and 144,

$$\Xi(H + Z) = \Xi(\eta_1 + \zeta_1) - \Xi(\eta_2 + \zeta_2) = (\Xi\eta_1 + \Xi\zeta_1) - (\Xi\eta_2 + \Xi\zeta_2),$$

and hence, by Theorems 185 and 200,

$$\Xi(H + Z) = (\Xi\eta_1 - \Xi\eta_2) + (\Xi\zeta_1 - \Xi\zeta_2) = \Xi(\eta_1 - \eta_2) + \Xi(\zeta_1 - \zeta_2)$$
$$= \Xi H + \Xi Z.$$

2) Let

$$\Xi = 0.$$

Then

$$\Xi(H + Z) = 0 = \Xi H + \Xi Z.$$

3) Let

$$\Xi < 0.$$

Then we have by 1) that

$$(-\Xi)(H + Z) = (-\Xi)H + (-\Xi)Z,$$

hence

$$-(\Xi(H + Z)) = (-\Xi)H + (-\Xi)Z,$$

$$\Xi(H + Z) = -((-\Xi)H + (-\Xi)Z) = -((-\Xi)H) + (-((-\Xi)Z))$$
$$= \Xi H + \Xi Z.$$

Theorem 202: $\Xi(H - Z) = \Xi H - \Xi Z.$

Proof: By Theorem 201, we have

$$\Xi(H - Z) = \Xi(H + (-Z)) = \Xi H + \Xi(-Z) = \Xi H + (-(\Xi Z))$$
$$= \Xi H - \Xi Z.$$

Theorem 203: *Let*

$$\Xi > H.$$

Then from

$$Z > 0 \,, \; or \; Z = 0 \,, \; or \; Z < 0 \,,$$

it follows that, respectively,

$$\Xi Z > HZ \,, \; or \; \Xi Z = HZ \,, \; or \; \Xi Z < HZ.$$

Proof:

$$\Xi - H > 0,$$

hence

$$(\Xi - H) Z > 0 \,, \text{ or } (\Xi - H) Z = 0 \,, \text{ or } (\Xi - H) Z < 0,$$

according to whether

$$Z > 0, \text{ or } Z = 0, \text{ or } Z < 0 \,,$$

respectively. Since we have by Theorem 202 that

$$(\Xi - H) Z = Z(\Xi - H) = Z\Xi - ZH = \Xi Z - HZ \,,$$

we have by Theorem 182 that in the above cases, respectively,

$$\Xi Z > HZ \,, \text{ or } \Xi Z = HZ \,, \text{ or } \Xi Z < HZ.$$

Theorem 204: *The equation*

$$HY = \Xi,$$

where Ξ, H *are given and where*

$$H \neq 0 \,,$$

has exactly one solution Y.

Proof: I) There is at most one solution; for if

$$HY_1 = \Xi = HY_2$$

then

$$0 = HY_1 - HY_2 = H(Y_1 - Y_2),$$

so that, by Theorem 192,

$$0 = Y_1 - Y_2,$$

$$Y_1 = Y_2.$$

II) 1) Let

$$H > 0.$$

Then

$$Y = \frac{1}{H}\Xi$$

is a solution, since

$$HY = H\left(\frac{1}{H}\Xi\right) = \left(H\frac{1}{H}\right)\Xi = 1 \cdot \Xi = \Xi.$$

2) Let

$$H < 0.$$

Then

$$Y = -\left(\frac{1}{|H|}\,\Xi\right)$$

is a solution; for we have from 1) that

$$\Xi = |H|\left(\frac{1}{|H|}\,\Xi\right) = |H|(-Y) = (-|H|)\,Y = HY.$$

Definition 56: *The* Y *of Theorem* 204 *is denoted by* $\frac{\Xi}{H}$ (to be read "Ξ over H"). *It is called the quotient of* Ξ *by* H, *or the number obtained from division of* Ξ *by* H.

Note that if $\Xi > 0$, $H > 0$, then this definition agrees (as it should) with the earlier Definition 38.

§ 5
Dedekind's Fundamental Theorem

Theorem 205: *Let there be given any division of all real numbers into two classes with the following properties:*

1) *There exists a number of the first class, and also one of the second class.*

2) *Every number of the first class is less than every number of the second class.*

Then there exists exactly one real number Ξ such that every $H < \Xi$ belongs to the first class and every $H > \Xi$ to the second class.

In other words, every number of the first class is $\leqq \Xi$ and every number of the second class is $\geqq \Xi$.

Preliminary Remark: It is obvious that, conversely, every real number Ξ gives rise to exactly two such divisions. One of these has as its first class all $H \leqq \Xi$ and as its second class all $H > \Xi$; the other one has as its first class all $H < \Xi$ and as its second class all $H \geqq \Xi$.

Proof: A) There can not be more than one such Ξ; for if we had

$$\Xi_1 < \Xi_2$$

and if Ξ_1 as well as Ξ_2 were as specified by Theorem 205, then the number $\frac{\Xi_1 + \Xi_2}{1+1}$ would have to belong both to the first and to the second class, since

$$(1+1)\Xi_1 = \Xi_1 + \Xi_1 < \Xi_1 + \Xi_2 < \Xi_2 + \Xi_2 = (1+1)\Xi_2,$$

$$\Xi_1 < \frac{\Xi_1 + \Xi_2}{1+1} < \Xi_2.$$

B) To prove the existence of a suitable Ξ, we distinguish four cases, as follows:

I) Suppose that the first class contains a positive number.

Consider the cut whose lower class contains all those positive rational numbers which lie in the first class of the given division, with the exception of the greatest such number if one exists; and whose upper class contains all the remaining positive rational numbers (i.e., contains all positive rational numbers of the second class, along with the greatest positive rational number of the first class, if any). This actually gives a cut, for:

1) Since the first class contains a positive number, it also contains every smaller positive rational number (and such do exist, by Theorem 158); hence it contains a positive rational number which is not the greatest therein. The lower class is therefore not empty.

Since the second class does contain a number, it also contains every greater positive rational number (and such do exist, by Theorem 158). The upper class is therefore not empty.

2) Every number of the lower class is less than every number of the upper class; for, every number of the first class is less than every number of the second class, and the greatest positive rational number of the first class (if any) is certainly greater than every number of the lower class.

3) The lower class does not contain a greatest positive rational number. For, the first class either does not contain such a greatest one, or if it does, then that number was assigned to the upper class; and we know from Theorem 91 that a set consisting of all positive rational numbers less than a given one does not contain a greatest.

We denote by Ξ the positive number defined by our cut, and we now assert that this Ξ satisfies the requirements of Theorem 205.

a) Consider any H such that

$$H < \Xi.$$

We choose, by Theorem 159 (with $\xi = H$, $\eta = \Xi$, in case $H > 0$; and with $\xi = \frac{\Xi}{1+1}$, $\eta = \Xi$, in case $H \leqq 0$), a Z such that

$$H < \mathrm{Z} < \Xi.$$

Then Z is a lower number for Ξ and hence belongs to the first class; therefore, so does H.

b) Consider any H such that

$$H > \Xi.$$

We choose a Z, by Theorem 159, such that

$$\Xi < \mathrm{Z} < H.$$

Then Z is an upper number for Ξ and (by Theorem 159) not the smallest such, so that it belongs to the second class; therefore, so does H.

II) Suppose that every positive number lies in the second class, and that 0 lies in the first class.

Then every negative number lies in the first class, and

$$\Xi = 0$$

satisfies the requirements.

III) Suppose that 0 lies in the second class, and that every negative number lies in the first class.

Then every positive number lies in the second class, and

$$\Xi = 0$$

satisfies the requirements.

IV) Suppose that there exists a negative number in the second class.

Then we consider the following new division:

Put H into the new first class if $-H$ was in the original second class;

put H into the new second class if $-H$ was in the original first class.

This new division evidently satisfies the two conditions of Theorem 205. For,

1) each of the new classes does contain a number;

2) if $$H_1 < H_2,$$
then, by Theorem 183, $-H_2 < -H_1$.

Moreover, the new division comes under case I), since the new first class does contain a positive number. Thus by I), there exists a number Ξ_1 such that every

$$H < \Xi_1$$

lies in the new first class, while every

$$H > \Xi_1$$

lies in the new second class. If we set

$$-\Xi_1 = \Xi,$$

then

$$H < \Xi, \text{ or } H > \Xi,$$

implies that

$$-H > \Xi_1, \text{ or } -H < \Xi_1, \text{ respectively.}$$

Hence $-H$ lies in the new second class, or new first class, respectively, so that H lies in the original first class, or original second class, respectively.

CHAPTER V

COMPLEX NUMBERS

§ 1

Definition

Definition 57: *A complex number is a pair of real numbers* Ξ_1, Ξ_2 (in a definite order). *We denote this complex number by* $[\Xi_1, \Xi_2]$. *Here,* $[\Xi_1, \Xi_2]$ *and* $[H_1, H_2]$ *are considered as the same number* (*as equal,* written "$=$") *if, and only if,*

$$\Xi_1 = H_1, \; \Xi_2 = H_2;$$

otherwise, they are considered as unequal (different; written "$\neq$").

Small German letters will stand throughout for complex numbers.

For every $\mathfrak{x}$ and every $\mathfrak{y}$, we thus have exactly one of the cases

$$\mathfrak{x} = \mathfrak{y}, \; \mathfrak{x} \neq \mathfrak{y}.$$

For the complex numbers, the concepts of identity and of equality are merged, so that the following three theorems are trivial:

Theorem 206: $$\mathfrak{x} = \mathfrak{x}.$$

Theorem 207: *If*

$$\mathfrak{x} = \mathfrak{y}$$

then

$$\mathfrak{y} = \mathfrak{x}.$$

Theorem 208: *If*

$$\mathfrak{x} = \mathfrak{y}, \quad \mathfrak{y} = \mathfrak{z}$$

then

$$\mathfrak{x} = \mathfrak{z}.$$

Definition 58: $$\mathfrak{n} = [0, 0].$$

Definition 59: $$\mathfrak{e} = [1, 0].$$

The letters $\mathfrak{n}$ and $\mathfrak{e}$ will thus be reserved for particular complex numbers.

§ 2
Addition

Definition 60: *If*

$$\mathfrak{x} = [\Xi_1, \Xi_2], \quad \mathfrak{y} = [H_1, H_2],$$

then

$$\mathfrak{x} + \mathfrak{y} = [\Xi_1 + H_1, \Xi_2 + H_2].$$

(+ to be read "plus.") $\mathfrak{x} + \mathfrak{y}$ *is called the sum of* $\mathfrak{x}$ *and* $\mathfrak{y}$, *or the* (complex) *number obtained by addition of* $\mathfrak{y}$ *to* $\mathfrak{x}$.

Theorem 209 (Commutative Law of Addition):

$$\mathfrak{x} + \mathfrak{y} = \mathfrak{y} + \mathfrak{x}.$$

Proof: $[\Xi_1 + H_1, \Xi_2 + H_2] = [H_1 + \Xi_1, H_2 + \Xi_2].$

Theorem 210: $\mathfrak{x} + \mathfrak{n} = \mathfrak{x}.$

Proof: $[\Xi_1, \Xi_2] + [0, 0] = [\Xi_1 + 0, \Xi_2 + 0] = [\Xi_1, \Xi_2].$

Theorem 211 (Associative Law of Addition):

$$(\mathfrak{x} + \mathfrak{y}) + \mathfrak{z} = \mathfrak{x} + (\mathfrak{y} + \mathfrak{z}).$$

Proof: If

$$\mathfrak{x} = [\Xi_1, \Xi_2], \quad \mathfrak{y} = [H_1, H_2], \quad \mathfrak{z} = [Z_1, Z_2],$$

then we have by Theorem 186 that

$$(\mathfrak{x} + \mathfrak{y}) + \mathfrak{z} = [\Xi_1 + H_1, \Xi_2 + H_2] + [Z_1, Z_2] = [(\Xi_1 + H_1) + Z_1, (\Xi_2 + H_2) + Z_2]$$
$$= [\Xi_1 + (H_1 + Z_1), \Xi_2 + (H_2 + Z_2)] = [\Xi_1, \Xi_2] + [H_1 + Z_1, H_2 + Z_2] = \mathfrak{x} + (\mathfrak{y} + \mathfrak{z}).$$

Theorem 212: *For any given* $\mathfrak{x}, \mathfrak{y}$, *the equation*

$$\mathfrak{y} + \mathfrak{u} = \mathfrak{x}$$

has exactly one solution $\mathfrak{u}$; *if we set*

$$\mathfrak{x} = [\Xi_1, \Xi_2], \quad \mathfrak{y} = [H_1, H_2],$$

then the solution is given by

$$\mathfrak{u} = [\Xi_1 - H_1, \Xi_2 - H_2].$$

Proof: For every

$$\mathfrak{u} = [Y_1, Y_2],$$

we have

$$\mathfrak{y} + \mathfrak{u} = [H_1 + Y_1, H_2 + Y_2],$$

and the requirements are exactly

$$H_1+Y_1 = \Xi_1, \quad H_2+Y_2 = \Xi_2,$$

so that Theorem 187 does the rest.

Definition 61: *The* $\mathfrak{u}$ *of Theorem* 212 *is denoted by* $\mathfrak{x}-\mathfrak{y}$ (— to be read "minus"). *It is called the difference* $\mathfrak{x}-\mathfrak{y}$, *or the number obtained by subtraction of* $\mathfrak{y}$ *from* $\mathfrak{x}$.

Theorem 213: *We have*

$$\mathfrak{x}-\mathfrak{y} = \mathfrak{n}$$

if, and only if,

$$\mathfrak{x} = \mathfrak{y}.$$

Proof: We have

$$\Xi_1 - H_1 = \Xi_2 - H_2 = 0$$

if, and only if,

$$\Xi_1 = H_1, \quad \Xi_2 = H_2.$$

Definition 62: $$-\mathfrak{x} = \mathfrak{n}-\mathfrak{x}.$$

(— on the left to be read "minus.")

Theorem 214: *If*

$$\mathfrak{x} = [\Xi_1, \Xi_2]$$

then

$$-\mathfrak{x} = [-\Xi_1, -\Xi_2].$$

Proof: $$-[\Xi_1, \Xi_2] = [0, 0]-[\Xi_1, \Xi_2] = [0-\Xi_1, 0-\Xi_2]$$
$$= [-\Xi_1, -\Xi_2].$$

Theorem 215: $$-(-\mathfrak{x}) = \mathfrak{x}.$$

Proof: By Theorem 177, we have

$$-(-\Xi_1) = \Xi_1, \quad -(-\Xi_2) = \Xi_2.$$

Theorem 216: $$\mathfrak{x}+(-\mathfrak{x}) = \mathfrak{n}.$$

Proof: By Theorem 179, we have

$$\Xi_1+(-\Xi_1) = 0, \; \Xi_2+(-\Xi_2) = 0.$$

Theorem 217: $$-(\mathfrak{x}+\mathfrak{y}) = -\mathfrak{x}+(-\mathfrak{y}).$$

Proof: By Theorem 180, we have, setting

$$\mathfrak{x} = [\Xi_1, \Xi_2], \quad \mathfrak{y} = [H_1, H_2],$$

that

$$-(\mathfrak{x}+\mathfrak{y}) = [-(\Xi_1+H_1),\ -(\Xi_2+H_2)] = [-\Xi_1+(-H_1),\ -\Xi_2+(-H_2)]$$
$$= [-\Xi_1,\ -\Xi_2]+[-H_1,\ -H_2] = -\mathfrak{x}+(-\mathfrak{y}).$$

Theorem 218: $\mathfrak{x}-\mathfrak{y} = \mathfrak{x}+(-\mathfrak{y}).$

Proof: $[\Xi_1-H_1,\ \Xi_2-H_2] = [\Xi_1,\ \Xi_2]+[-H_1,\ -H_2].$

Theorem 219: $-(\mathfrak{x}-\mathfrak{y}) = \mathfrak{y}-\mathfrak{x}.$

Proof: $-(\mathfrak{x}-\mathfrak{y}) = -(\mathfrak{x}+(-\mathfrak{y})) = -\mathfrak{x}+(-(-\mathfrak{y})) = -\mathfrak{x}+\mathfrak{y}$
$= \mathfrak{y}+(-\mathfrak{x}) = \mathfrak{y}-\mathfrak{x}.$

§ 3

Multiplication

Definition 63: *If*

$$\mathfrak{x} = [\Xi_1, \Xi_2], \quad \mathfrak{y} = [H_1, H_2],$$

then

$$\mathfrak{x} \cdot \mathfrak{y} = [\Xi_1 H_1 - \Xi_2 H_2, \ \Xi_1 H_2 + \Xi_2 H_1].$$

(• to be read "times"; however, the dot is usually omitted.) $\mathfrak{x} \cdot \mathfrak{y}$ *is called the product of* $\mathfrak{x}$ *and* $\mathfrak{y}$, *or the number obtained from multiplication of* $\mathfrak{x}$ *by* $\mathfrak{y}$.

Theorem 220 (Commutative Law of Multiplication):

$$\mathfrak{x}\mathfrak{y} = \mathfrak{y}\mathfrak{x}.$$

Proof: $[\Xi_1, \Xi_2][H_1, H_2] = [\Xi_1 H_1 - \Xi_2 H_2, \ \Xi_1 H_2 + \Xi_2 H_1]$

$$= [H_1 \Xi_1 - H_2 \Xi_2, \ H_1 \Xi_2 + H_2 \Xi_1] = [H_1, H_2][\Xi_1, \Xi_2].$$

Theorem 221: *We have*

$$\mathfrak{x}\mathfrak{y} = \mathfrak{n}$$

if, and only if, at least one of the two numbers $\mathfrak{x}$, $\mathfrak{y}$ *is equal to* $\mathfrak{n}$.

Proof: Let

$$\mathfrak{x} = [\Xi_1, \Xi_2], \quad \mathfrak{y} = [H_1, H_2].$$

1) If

$$\mathfrak{x} = \mathfrak{n}$$

then

$$\Xi_1 = \Xi_2 = 0,$$

$$\mathfrak{x}\mathfrak{y} = [0 \cdot H_1 - 0 \cdot H_2, \ 0 \cdot H_2 + 0 \cdot H_1] = [0, 0] = \mathfrak{n}.$$

2) If

$$\mathfrak{y} = \mathfrak{n}$$

then, by Theorem 220 and by 1),

$$\mathfrak{x}\mathfrak{y} = \mathfrak{y}\mathfrak{x} = \mathfrak{n}\mathfrak{x} = \mathfrak{n}.$$

3) We are to infer from

$$\mathfrak{x}\mathfrak{y} = \mathfrak{n}$$

that

$$\mathfrak{x} = \mathfrak{n} \text{ or } \mathfrak{y} = \mathfrak{n}.$$

We may therefore assume that

$$\mathfrak{y} \neq \mathfrak{n},$$

i.e. that

$$H_1 H_1 + H_2 H_2 > 0,$$

and we have to prove that

$$\mathfrak{x} = \mathfrak{n},$$

holds, i.e. that

$$\Xi_1 = \Xi_2 = 0$$

holds.

By hypothesis, we have

$$\Xi_1 H_1 - \Xi_2 H_2 = 0 = \Xi_1 H_2 + \Xi_2 H_1,$$

hence

$$\begin{aligned} 0 &= (\Xi_1 H_1 - \Xi_2 H_2) H_1 + (\Xi_1 H_2 + \Xi_2 H_1) H_2 \\ &= ((\Xi_1 H_1) H_1 - (\Xi_2 H_2) H_1) + ((\Xi_1 H_2) H_2 + (\Xi_2 H_1) H_2) \\ &= (\Xi_1 (H_1 H_1) - \Xi_2 (H_2 H_1)) + (\Xi_1 (H_2 H_2) + \Xi_2 (H_1 H_2)) \\ &= ((\Xi_1 (H_1 H_1) - \Xi_2 (H_1 H_2)) + \Xi_2 (H_1 H_2)) + \Xi_1 (H_2 H_2) \\ &= \Xi_1 (H_1 H_1) + \Xi_1 (H_2 H_2) = \Xi_1 (H_1 H_1 + H_2 H_2), \end{aligned}$$

so that

$$\Xi_1 = 0,$$

$$\Xi_2 H_2 = 0 = \Xi_2 H_1.$$

Since H_1 and H_2 are not both 0, we therefore have

$$\Xi_2 = 0.$$

Theorem 222: $$\mathfrak{x}\mathfrak{e} = \mathfrak{x}.$$

Proof: $$[\Xi_1, \Xi_2][1, 0] = [\Xi_1 \cdot 1 - \Xi_2 \cdot 0, \Xi_1 \cdot 0 + \Xi_2 \cdot 1] = [\Xi_1, \Xi_2].$$

Theorem 223: $$\mathfrak{x}(-\mathfrak{e}) = -\mathfrak{x}.$$

Proof: $$\begin{aligned} [\Xi_1, \Xi_2][-1, 0] &= [\Xi_1(-1) - \Xi_2 \cdot 0, \ \Xi_1 \cdot 0 + \Xi_2(-1)] \\ &= [-\Xi_1, -\Xi_2]. \end{aligned}$$

Theorem 224: $$(-\mathfrak{x})\mathfrak{y} = \mathfrak{x}(-\mathfrak{y}) = -(\mathfrak{x}\mathfrak{y}).$$

Proof: 1)

$$\begin{aligned} [-\Xi_1, -\Xi_2][H_1, H_2] &= [(-\Xi_1) H_1 - (-\Xi_2) H_2, \ (-\Xi_1) H_2 + (-\Xi_2) H_1] \\ &= [-(\Xi_1 H_1) + \Xi_2 H_2, \ -(\Xi_1 H_2) - \Xi_2 H_1] \\ &= [-(\Xi_1 H_1 - \Xi_2 H_2), \ -(\Xi_1 H_2 + \Xi_2 H_1)] \\ &= -([\Xi_1, \Xi_2][H_1, H_2]), \end{aligned}$$

$$(-\mathfrak{x})\mathfrak{y} = -(\mathfrak{x}\mathfrak{y}).$$

2) By 1), we have

$$\mathfrak{x}(-\mathfrak{y}) = (-\mathfrak{y})\mathfrak{x} = -(\mathfrak{y}\mathfrak{x}) = -(\mathfrak{x}\mathfrak{y}).$$

Theorem 225: $$(-\mathfrak{x})(-\mathfrak{y}) = \mathfrak{x}\mathfrak{y}.$$

Proof: By Theorem 224, we have

$$(-\mathfrak{x})(-\mathfrak{y}) = \mathfrak{x}(-(-\mathfrak{y})) = \mathfrak{x}\mathfrak{y}.$$

Theorem 226 (Associative Law of Multiplication):

$$(\mathfrak{x}\mathfrak{y})\mathfrak{z} = \mathfrak{x}(\mathfrak{y}\mathfrak{z}).$$

Proof: As an exception, and for the sake of making the writing more concise, we set, by way of abbreviations,

$$(\Xi + H) + Z = \Xi + H + Z,$$
$$(\Xi H)Z = \Xi H Z$$

so that

$$\Xi + (H + Z) = \Xi + H + Z,$$
$$\Xi(HZ) = \Xi H Z$$

will also hold.

Set

$$\mathfrak{x} = [\Xi_1, \Xi_2], \quad \mathfrak{y} = [H_1, H_2], \quad \mathfrak{z} = [Z_1, Z_2].$$

Then we have

$$\begin{aligned}(\mathfrak{x}\mathfrak{y})\mathfrak{z} &= [\Xi_1 H_1 - \Xi_2 H_2, \ \Xi_1 H_2 + \Xi_2 H_1][Z_1, Z_2]\\ &= [(\Xi_1 H_1 - \Xi_2 H_2) Z_1 - (\Xi_1 H_2 + \Xi_2 H_1) Z_2,\\ &\quad (\Xi_1 H_1 - \Xi_2 H_2) Z_2 + (\Xi_1 H_2 + \Xi_2 H_1) Z_1]\\ &= [(\Xi_1 H_1 Z_1 - \Xi_2 H_2 Z_1) - (\Xi_1 H_2 Z_2 + \Xi_2 H_1 Z_2),\\ &\quad (\Xi_1 H_1 Z_2 - \Xi_2 H_2 Z_2) + (\Xi_1 H_2 Z_1 + \Xi_2 H_1 Z_1)]\\ &= [(\Xi_1 H_1 Z_1 + (-(\Xi_2 H_2 Z_1))) + (-(\Xi_1 H_2 Z_2 + \Xi_2 H_1 Z_2)),\\ &\quad (\Xi_1 H_2 Z_1 + \Xi_2 H_1 Z_1) + (\Xi_1 H_1 Z_2 + (-(\Xi_2 H_2 Z_2)))]\\ &= [\Xi_1 H_1 Z_1 - (\Xi_2 H_2 Z_1 + \Xi_1 H_2 Z_2 + \Xi_2 H_1 Z_2),\\ &\quad (\Xi_1 H_2 Z_1 + \Xi_2 H_1 Z_1 + \Xi_1 H_1 Z_2) - \Xi_2 H_2 Z_2].\end{aligned}$$

Since

$$\mathfrak{x}(\mathfrak{y}\mathfrak{z}) = (\mathfrak{y}\mathfrak{z})\mathfrak{x},$$

we obtain by an interchange of letters (H for Ξ, Z for H, Ξ for Z) that

$$\begin{aligned}\mathfrak{x}(\mathfrak{y}\mathfrak{z}) = [&H_1 Z_1 \Xi_1 - (H_2 Z_2 \Xi_1 + H_1 Z_2 \Xi_2 + H_2 Z_1 \Xi_2),\\ &(H_1 Z_2 \Xi_1 + H_2 Z_1 \Xi_1 + H_1 Z_1 \Xi_2) - H_2 Z_2 \Xi_2].\end{aligned}$$

Since

$$\Xi H Z = \Xi(HZ) = (HZ)\Xi = HZ\Xi,$$
$$A + B + \Gamma = A + (B + \Gamma) = (B + \Gamma) + A = B + \Gamma + A,$$

we see from the expressions just calculated that

$$(\mathfrak{x}\mathfrak{y})\mathfrak{z} = \mathfrak{x}(\mathfrak{y}\mathfrak{z}).$$

Theorem 227 (Distributive Law):

$$\mathfrak{x}(\mathfrak{y}+\mathfrak{z}) = \mathfrak{x}\mathfrak{y}+\mathfrak{x}\mathfrak{z}.$$

Proof:

$$[\Xi_1, \Xi_2]([H_1, H_2]+[Z_1, Z_2]) = [\Xi_1, \Xi_2][H_1+Z_1, H_2+Z_2]$$
$$= [\Xi_1(H_1+Z_1)-\Xi_2(H_2+Z_2), \Xi_1(H_2+Z_2)+\Xi_2(H_1+Z_1)]$$
$$= [(\Xi_1 H_1+\Xi_1 Z_1)+(-(\Xi_2 H_2)+(-(\Xi_2 Z_2))), (\Xi_1 H_2+\Xi_1 Z_2)+(\Xi_2 H_1+\Xi_2 Z_1)]$$
$$= [(\Xi_1 H_1-\Xi_2 H_2)+(\Xi_1 Z_1-\Xi_2 Z_2), (\Xi_1 H_2+\Xi_2 H_1)+(\Xi_1 Z_2+\Xi_2 Z_1)]$$
$$= [\Xi_1 H_1-\Xi_2 H_2, \Xi_1 H_2+\Xi_2 H_1]+[\Xi_1 Z_1-\Xi_2 Z_2, \Xi_1 Z_2+\Xi_2 Z_1]$$
$$= [\Xi_1, \Xi_2][H_1, H_2]+[\Xi_1, \Xi_2][Z_1, Z_2].$$

Theorem 228: $\mathfrak{x}(\mathfrak{y}-\mathfrak{z}) = \mathfrak{x}\mathfrak{y}-\mathfrak{x}\mathfrak{z}.$

Proof: $\mathfrak{x}(\mathfrak{y}-\mathfrak{z}) = \mathfrak{x}(\mathfrak{y}+(-\mathfrak{z})) = \mathfrak{x}\mathfrak{y}+\mathfrak{x}(-\mathfrak{z}) = \mathfrak{x}\mathfrak{y}+(-(\mathfrak{x}\mathfrak{z}))$
$$= \mathfrak{x}\mathfrak{y}-\mathfrak{x}\mathfrak{z}.$$

Theorem 229: *The equation*

$$\mathfrak{y}\mathfrak{u} = \mathfrak{x},$$

where $\mathfrak{x}$ *and* $\mathfrak{y}$ *are given and where*

$$\mathfrak{y} \neq \mathfrak{n},$$

has exactly one solution $\mathfrak{u}$.

Proof: 1) There is at most one solution; for if

$$\mathfrak{y}\mathfrak{u}_1 = \mathfrak{x} = \mathfrak{y}\mathfrak{u}_2$$

then

$$\mathfrak{n} = \mathfrak{y}\mathfrak{u}_1-\mathfrak{y}\mathfrak{u}_2 = \mathfrak{y}(\mathfrak{u}_1-\mathfrak{u}_2),$$

so that, by Theorem 221,

$$\mathfrak{n} = \mathfrak{u}_1-\mathfrak{u}_2,$$
$$\mathfrak{u}_1 = \mathfrak{u}_2.$$

2) If

$$\mathfrak{y} = [H_1, H_2],$$

then

$$H = H_1 H_1 + H_2 H_2 > 0,$$

and

$$\mathfrak{u} = \left[\frac{H_1}{H}, -\frac{H_2}{H}\right]\mathfrak{x}$$

is a solution, since

$$\mathfrak{y}\mathfrak{u} = \left([H_1, H_2]\left[\frac{H_1}{H}, -\frac{H_2}{H}\right]\right)\mathfrak{x}$$

$$= \left[H_1\frac{H_1}{H} + H_2\frac{H_2}{H}, -\left(H_1\frac{H_2}{H}\right) + H_2\frac{H_1}{H}\right]\mathfrak{x}$$

$$= \left[\frac{H_1 H_1 + H_2 H_2}{H}, \frac{-(H_1 H_2) + H_1 H_2}{H}\right]\mathfrak{x} = [1, 0]\mathfrak{x} = \mathfrak{e}\mathfrak{x} = \mathfrak{x}.$$

Definition 64: *The* $\mathfrak{u}$ *of Theorem* 229 *is denoted by* $\frac{\mathfrak{x}}{\mathfrak{y}}$ (to be read "$\mathfrak{x}$ over $\mathfrak{y}$"). *It is called the quotient of* $\mathfrak{x}$ *by* $\mathfrak{y}$, *or the number obtained from division of* $\mathfrak{x}$ *by* $\mathfrak{y}$.

§ 4

Subtraction

Theorem 230: $$(\mathfrak{x}-\mathfrak{y})+\mathfrak{y} = \mathfrak{x}.$$

Proof: $$(\mathfrak{x}-\mathfrak{y})+\mathfrak{y} = \mathfrak{y}+(\mathfrak{x}-\mathfrak{y}) = \mathfrak{x}.$$

Theorem 231: $$(\mathfrak{x}+\mathfrak{y})-\mathfrak{y} = \mathfrak{x}.$$

Proof: $$\mathfrak{y}+\mathfrak{x} = \mathfrak{x}+\mathfrak{y}.$$

Theorem 232: $$\mathfrak{x}-(\mathfrak{x}-\mathfrak{y}) = \mathfrak{y}.$$

Proof: $$(\mathfrak{x}-\mathfrak{y})+\mathfrak{y} = \mathfrak{x}.$$

Theorem 233: $$(\mathfrak{x}-\mathfrak{y})-\mathfrak{z} = \mathfrak{x}-(\mathfrak{y}+\mathfrak{z}).$$

Proof: $$(\mathfrak{y}+\mathfrak{z})+((\mathfrak{x}-\mathfrak{y})-\mathfrak{z}) = ((\mathfrak{x}-\mathfrak{y})-\mathfrak{z})+(\mathfrak{z}+\mathfrak{y})$$
$$= (((\mathfrak{x}-\mathfrak{y})-\mathfrak{z})+\mathfrak{z})+\mathfrak{y} = (\mathfrak{x}-\mathfrak{y})+\mathfrak{y} = \mathfrak{x}.$$

Theorem 234: $$(\mathfrak{x}+\mathfrak{y})-\mathfrak{z} = \mathfrak{x}+(\mathfrak{y}-\mathfrak{z}).$$

Proof: $$(\mathfrak{x}+(\mathfrak{y}-\mathfrak{z}))+\mathfrak{z} = \mathfrak{x}+((\mathfrak{y}-\mathfrak{z})+\mathfrak{z}) = \mathfrak{x}+\mathfrak{y}.$$

Theorem 235: $$(\mathfrak{x}-\mathfrak{y})+\mathfrak{z} = \mathfrak{x}-(\mathfrak{y}-\mathfrak{z}).$$

Proof: $$((\mathfrak{x}-\mathfrak{y})+\mathfrak{z})+(\mathfrak{y}-\mathfrak{z}) = (\mathfrak{x}-\mathfrak{y})+(\mathfrak{z}+(\mathfrak{y}-\mathfrak{z}))$$
$$= (\mathfrak{x}-\mathfrak{y})+\mathfrak{y} = \mathfrak{x}.$$

Theorem 236: $$(\mathfrak{x}+\mathfrak{z})-(\mathfrak{y}+\mathfrak{z}) = \mathfrak{x}-\mathfrak{y}.$$

Proof: $$(\mathfrak{x}-\mathfrak{y})+(\mathfrak{y}+\mathfrak{z}) = ((\mathfrak{x}-\mathfrak{y})+\mathfrak{y})+\mathfrak{z} = \mathfrak{x}+\mathfrak{z}.$$

Theorem 237: $$(\mathfrak{x}-\mathfrak{y})+(\mathfrak{z}-\mathfrak{u}) = (\mathfrak{x}+\mathfrak{z})-(\mathfrak{y}+\mathfrak{u}).$$

Proof: $$((\mathfrak{x}-\mathfrak{y})+(\mathfrak{z}-\mathfrak{u}))+(\mathfrak{y}+\mathfrak{u}) = (\mathfrak{x}-\mathfrak{y})+((\mathfrak{z}-\mathfrak{u})+(\mathfrak{u}+\mathfrak{y}))$$
$$= (\mathfrak{x}-\mathfrak{y})+(((\mathfrak{z}-\mathfrak{u})+\mathfrak{u})+\mathfrak{y}) = (\mathfrak{x}-\mathfrak{y})+(\mathfrak{z}+\mathfrak{y}) = (\mathfrak{x}-\mathfrak{y})+(\mathfrak{y}+\mathfrak{z})$$
$$= ((\mathfrak{x}-\mathfrak{y})+\mathfrak{y})+\mathfrak{z} = \mathfrak{x}+\mathfrak{z}.$$

Theorem 238: $$(\mathfrak{x}-\mathfrak{y})-(\mathfrak{z}-\mathfrak{u}) = (\mathfrak{x}+\mathfrak{u})-(\mathfrak{y}+\mathfrak{z}).$$

Proof: By Theorems 237 and 236, we have
$$((\mathfrak{x}+\mathfrak{u})-(\mathfrak{y}+\mathfrak{z}))+(\mathfrak{z}-\mathfrak{u}) = ((\mathfrak{x}+\mathfrak{u})+\mathfrak{z})-((\mathfrak{y}+\mathfrak{z})+\mathfrak{u})$$
$$= (\mathfrak{x}+(\mathfrak{u}+\mathfrak{z}))-(\mathfrak{y}+(\mathfrak{z}+\mathfrak{u})) = \mathfrak{x}-\mathfrak{y}.$$

Theorem 239: *We have*
$$\mathfrak{x}-\mathfrak{y} = \mathfrak{z}-\mathfrak{u}$$
if, and only if,
$$\mathfrak{x}+\mathfrak{u} = \mathfrak{y}+\mathfrak{z}.$$

Proof: Theorems 213 and 238.

---

§ 5

Division

Theorem 240: *If*

$$\mathfrak{y} \neq \mathfrak{n},$$

then

$$\frac{\mathfrak{x}}{\mathfrak{y}}\mathfrak{y} = \mathfrak{x}.$$

Proof:

$$\frac{\mathfrak{x}}{\mathfrak{y}}\mathfrak{y} = \mathfrak{y}\frac{\mathfrak{x}}{\mathfrak{y}} = \mathfrak{x}.$$

Theorem 241: *If*

$$\mathfrak{y} \neq \mathfrak{n},$$

then

$$\frac{\mathfrak{x}\mathfrak{y}}{\mathfrak{y}} = \mathfrak{x}.$$

Proof:

$$\mathfrak{y}\mathfrak{x} = \mathfrak{x}\mathfrak{y}.$$

Theorem 242: *If*

$$\mathfrak{x} \neq \mathfrak{n}, \quad \mathfrak{y} \neq \mathfrak{n},$$

then

$$\frac{\mathfrak{x}}{\frac{\mathfrak{x}}{\mathfrak{y}}} = \mathfrak{y}.$$

Proof:

$$\frac{\mathfrak{x}}{\mathfrak{y}}\mathfrak{y} = \mathfrak{x}.$$

Theorem 243: *If*

$$\mathfrak{y} \neq \mathfrak{n}, \quad \mathfrak{z} \neq \mathfrak{n},$$

then

$$\frac{\frac{\mathfrak{x}}{\mathfrak{y}}}{\mathfrak{z}} = \frac{\mathfrak{x}}{\mathfrak{y}\mathfrak{z}}.$$

Proof:

$$(\mathfrak{y}\mathfrak{z})\frac{\frac{\mathfrak{x}}{\mathfrak{y}}}{\mathfrak{z}} = \frac{\frac{\mathfrak{x}}{\mathfrak{y}}}{\mathfrak{z}}(\mathfrak{z}\mathfrak{y}) = \left(\frac{\frac{\mathfrak{x}}{\mathfrak{y}}}{\mathfrak{z}}\mathfrak{z}\right)\mathfrak{y} = \frac{\mathfrak{x}}{\mathfrak{y}}\mathfrak{y} = \mathfrak{x}.$$

Theorem 244: *If*

$$\mathfrak{z} \neq \mathfrak{n},$$

then

$$\frac{\mathfrak{x}\mathfrak{y}}{\mathfrak{z}} = \mathfrak{x}\frac{\mathfrak{y}}{\mathfrak{z}}.$$

Proof: $$\left(\mathfrak{x}\frac{\mathfrak{y}}{\mathfrak{z}}\right)\mathfrak{z} = \mathfrak{x}\left(\frac{\mathfrak{y}}{\mathfrak{z}}\mathfrak{z}\right) = \mathfrak{x}\mathfrak{y}.$$

Theorem 245: *If*

$$\mathfrak{y} \neq \mathfrak{n},\quad \mathfrak{z} \neq \mathfrak{n},$$

then

$$\frac{\mathfrak{x}}{\mathfrak{y}}\mathfrak{z} = \frac{\mathfrak{x}}{\frac{\mathfrak{y}}{\mathfrak{z}}}.$$

Proof: $$\left(\frac{\mathfrak{x}}{\mathfrak{y}}\mathfrak{z}\right)\frac{\mathfrak{y}}{\mathfrak{z}} = \frac{\mathfrak{x}}{\mathfrak{y}}\left(\mathfrak{z}\frac{\mathfrak{y}}{\mathfrak{z}}\right) = \frac{\mathfrak{x}}{\mathfrak{y}}\mathfrak{y} = \mathfrak{x}.$$

Theorem 246: *If*

$$\mathfrak{y} \neq \mathfrak{n},\quad \mathfrak{z} \neq \mathfrak{n},$$

then

$$\frac{\mathfrak{x}\mathfrak{z}}{\mathfrak{y}\mathfrak{z}} = \frac{\mathfrak{x}}{\mathfrak{y}}.$$

Proof: $$\frac{\mathfrak{x}}{\mathfrak{y}}(\mathfrak{y}\mathfrak{z}) = \left(\frac{\mathfrak{x}}{\mathfrak{y}}\mathfrak{y}\right)\mathfrak{z} = \mathfrak{x}\mathfrak{z}.$$

Theorem 247: *If*

$$\mathfrak{y} \neq \mathfrak{n},\quad \mathfrak{u} \neq \mathfrak{n},$$

then

$$\frac{\mathfrak{x}}{\mathfrak{y}}\cdot\frac{\mathfrak{z}}{\mathfrak{u}} = \frac{\mathfrak{x}\mathfrak{z}}{\mathfrak{y}\mathfrak{u}}.$$

Proof: $$\left(\frac{\mathfrak{x}}{\mathfrak{y}}\cdot\frac{\mathfrak{z}}{\mathfrak{u}}\right)(\mathfrak{y}\mathfrak{u}) = \frac{\mathfrak{x}}{\mathfrak{y}}\left(\frac{\mathfrak{z}}{\mathfrak{u}}(\mathfrak{u}\mathfrak{y})\right) = \frac{\mathfrak{x}}{\mathfrak{y}}\left(\left(\frac{\mathfrak{z}}{\mathfrak{u}}\mathfrak{u}\right)\mathfrak{y}\right)$$
$$= \frac{\mathfrak{x}}{\mathfrak{y}}(\mathfrak{z}\mathfrak{y}) = \frac{\mathfrak{x}}{\mathfrak{y}}(\mathfrak{y}\mathfrak{z}) = \left(\frac{\mathfrak{x}}{\mathfrak{y}}\mathfrak{y}\right)\mathfrak{z} = \mathfrak{x}\mathfrak{z}.$$

Theorem 248: *If*

$$\mathfrak{y} \neq \mathfrak{n},\quad \mathfrak{z} \neq \mathfrak{n},\quad \mathfrak{u} \neq \mathfrak{n},$$

then

$$\frac{\frac{\mathfrak{x}}{\mathfrak{y}}}{\frac{\mathfrak{z}}{\mathfrak{u}}} = \frac{\mathfrak{x}\mathfrak{u}}{\mathfrak{y}\mathfrak{z}}.$$

Proof: By Theorems 247 and 246, we have

$$\frac{\mathfrak{x}\mathfrak{u}}{\mathfrak{y}\mathfrak{z}}\cdot\frac{\mathfrak{z}}{\mathfrak{u}} = \frac{(\mathfrak{x}\mathfrak{u})\mathfrak{z}}{(\mathfrak{y}\mathfrak{z})\mathfrak{u}} = \frac{\mathfrak{x}(\mathfrak{u}\mathfrak{z})}{\mathfrak{y}(\mathfrak{z}\mathfrak{u})} = \frac{\mathfrak{x}}{\mathfrak{y}}.$$

Theorem 249: *If*

$$\mathfrak{x} \neq \mathfrak{n},$$

then

$$\frac{\mathfrak{n}}{\mathfrak{x}} = \mathfrak{n}.$$

Proof:

$$\mathfrak{x}\mathfrak{n} = \mathfrak{n}.$$

Theorem 250: *If*

$$\mathfrak{x} \neq \mathfrak{n},$$

then

$$\frac{\mathfrak{x}}{\mathfrak{x}} = \mathfrak{e}.$$

Proof:

$$\mathfrak{x}\mathfrak{e} = \mathfrak{x}.$$

Theorem 251: *If*

$$\mathfrak{y} \neq \mathfrak{n},$$

then

$$\frac{\mathfrak{x}}{\mathfrak{y}} = \mathfrak{e}$$

if, and only if,

$$\mathfrak{x} = \mathfrak{y}.$$

Proof: 1) If

$$\mathfrak{x} = \mathfrak{y},$$

then, by Theorem 250,

$$\frac{\mathfrak{x}}{\mathfrak{y}} = \frac{\mathfrak{y}}{\mathfrak{y}} = \mathfrak{e}.$$

2) If

$$\frac{\mathfrak{x}}{\mathfrak{y}} = \mathfrak{e},$$

then, by Theorem 222,

$$\mathfrak{x} = \mathfrak{y}\mathfrak{e} = \mathfrak{y}.$$

Theorem 252: *If*

$$\mathfrak{y} \neq \mathfrak{n}, \quad \mathfrak{u} \neq \mathfrak{n},$$

then

$$\frac{\mathfrak{x}}{\mathfrak{y}} = \frac{\mathfrak{z}}{\mathfrak{u}}$$

if, and only if,

$$\mathfrak{x}\mathfrak{u} = \mathfrak{y}\mathfrak{z}.$$

Proof: For the case

$$\mathfrak{z} = \mathfrak{n},$$

the assertion is obvious.

Otherwise, we have by Theorem 248 that

$$\frac{\frac{\mathfrak{x}}{\mathfrak{y}}}{\frac{\mathfrak{z}}{\mathfrak{u}}} = \frac{\mathfrak{x}\mathfrak{u}}{\mathfrak{y}\mathfrak{z}},$$

so that Theorem 251 now proves the assertion.

Theorem 253: *If*

$$\mathfrak{y} \neq \mathfrak{n},$$

then

$$\frac{\mathfrak{x}}{\mathfrak{y}} + \frac{\mathfrak{z}}{\mathfrak{y}} = \frac{\mathfrak{x}+\mathfrak{z}}{\mathfrak{y}}.$$

Proof:

$$\mathfrak{y}\left(\frac{\mathfrak{x}}{\mathfrak{y}} + \frac{\mathfrak{z}}{\mathfrak{y}}\right) = \mathfrak{y}\frac{\mathfrak{x}}{\mathfrak{y}} + \mathfrak{y}\frac{\mathfrak{z}}{\mathfrak{y}} = \mathfrak{x}+\mathfrak{z}.$$

Theorem 254: *If*

$$\mathfrak{y} \neq \mathfrak{n}, \quad \mathfrak{u} \neq \mathfrak{n},$$

then

$$\frac{\mathfrak{x}}{\mathfrak{y}} + \frac{\mathfrak{z}}{\mathfrak{u}} = \frac{\mathfrak{x}\mathfrak{u}+\mathfrak{y}\mathfrak{z}}{\mathfrak{y}\mathfrak{u}}.$$

Proof: By Theorems 246 and 253, we have

$$\frac{\mathfrak{x}}{\mathfrak{y}} + \frac{\mathfrak{z}}{\mathfrak{u}} = \frac{\mathfrak{x}\mathfrak{u}}{\mathfrak{y}\mathfrak{u}} + \frac{\mathfrak{y}\mathfrak{z}}{\mathfrak{y}\mathfrak{u}} = \frac{\mathfrak{x}\mathfrak{u}+\mathfrak{y}\mathfrak{z}}{\mathfrak{y}\mathfrak{u}}.$$

Theorem 255: *If*

$$\mathfrak{y} \neq \mathfrak{n},$$

then

$$\frac{\mathfrak{x}}{\mathfrak{y}} - \frac{\mathfrak{z}}{\mathfrak{y}} = \frac{\mathfrak{x}-\mathfrak{z}}{\mathfrak{y}}.$$

Proof:

$$\mathfrak{y}\left(\frac{\mathfrak{x}}{\mathfrak{y}} - \frac{\mathfrak{z}}{\mathfrak{y}}\right) = \mathfrak{y}\frac{\mathfrak{x}}{\mathfrak{y}} - \mathfrak{y}\frac{\mathfrak{z}}{\mathfrak{y}} = \mathfrak{x}-\mathfrak{z}.$$

Theorem 256: *If*

$$\mathfrak{y} \neq \mathfrak{n}, \quad \mathfrak{u} \neq \mathfrak{n},$$

then

$$\frac{\mathfrak{x}}{\mathfrak{y}} - \frac{\mathfrak{z}}{\mathfrak{u}} = \frac{\mathfrak{x}\mathfrak{u}-\mathfrak{y}\mathfrak{z}}{\mathfrak{y}\mathfrak{u}}.$$

Proof: By Theorems 246 and 255, we have

$$\frac{\mathfrak{x}}{\mathfrak{y}} - \frac{\mathfrak{z}}{\mathfrak{u}} = \frac{\mathfrak{x}\mathfrak{u}}{\mathfrak{y}\mathfrak{u}} - \frac{\mathfrak{y}\mathfrak{z}}{\mathfrak{y}\mathfrak{u}} = \frac{\mathfrak{x}\mathfrak{u}-\mathfrak{y}\mathfrak{z}}{\mathfrak{y}\mathfrak{u}}.$$

§ 6

Complex Conjugates

Definition 65: *Given*

$$\mathfrak{x} = [\Xi_1, \Xi_2],$$

then the number

$$\bar{\mathfrak{x}} = [\Xi_1, -\Xi_2]$$

is called the complex conjugate of $\mathfrak{x}$.

Theorem 257: $$\bar{\bar{\mathfrak{x}}} = \mathfrak{x}.$$

Proof: $$[\Xi_1, -(-\Xi_2)] = [\Xi_1, \Xi_2].$$

Theorem 258: *We have*

$$\bar{\mathfrak{x}} = \mathfrak{n}$$

if, and only if,

$$\mathfrak{x} = \mathfrak{n}.$$

Proof: $$\Xi_{.} = 0, \quad -\Xi_2 = 0$$

is the same as

$$\Xi_1 = 0, \quad \Xi_2 = 0.$$

Theorem 259: *We have*

$$\bar{\mathfrak{x}} = \mathfrak{x}$$

if, and only if, $\mathfrak{x}$ *is of the form*

$$\mathfrak{x} = [\Xi, 0].$$

Proof: We have

$$\Xi_1 = \Xi_1, \quad -\Xi_2 = \Xi_2$$

if, and only if,

$$\Xi_2 = 0.$$

Theorem 260: $$\overline{\mathfrak{x}+\mathfrak{y}} = \bar{\mathfrak{x}} + \bar{\mathfrak{y}}.$$

Proof: If

$$\mathfrak{x} = [\Xi_1, \Xi_2], \quad \mathfrak{y} = [H_1, H_2],$$

then

$$\overline{\mathfrak{x}+\mathfrak{y}} = [\Xi_1 + H_1, -(\Xi_2 + H_2)] = [\Xi_1 + H_1, -\Xi_2 + (-H_2)]$$
$$= [\Xi_1, -\Xi_2] + [H_1, -H_2] = \bar{\mathfrak{x}} + \bar{\mathfrak{y}}.$$

Theorem 261: $$\overline{\mathfrak{x}\mathfrak{y}} = \overline{\mathfrak{x}}\,\overline{\mathfrak{y}}.$$

Proof: If

$$\mathfrak{x} = [\Xi_1, \Xi_2], \quad \mathfrak{y} = [H_1, H_2],$$

then

$$\begin{aligned}\overline{\mathfrak{x}\mathfrak{y}} &= [\Xi_1 H_1 - \Xi_2 H_2, \ -(\Xi_1 H_2 + \Xi_2 H_1)] \\ &= [\Xi_1 H_1 - (-\Xi_2)(-H_2), \ \Xi_1(-H_2) + (-\Xi_2) H_1] \\ &= [\Xi_1, -\Xi_2][H_1, -H_2] = \overline{\mathfrak{x}}\,\overline{\mathfrak{y}}.\end{aligned}$$

Theorem 262: $$\overline{\mathfrak{x} - \mathfrak{y}} = \overline{\mathfrak{x}} - \overline{\mathfrak{y}}.$$

Proof: Since

$$\mathfrak{x} = (\mathfrak{x} - \mathfrak{y}) + \mathfrak{y},$$

we have, by Theorem 260, that

$$\overline{\mathfrak{x}} = \overline{\mathfrak{x} - \mathfrak{y}} + \overline{\mathfrak{y}},$$

$$\overline{\mathfrak{x} - \mathfrak{y}} = \overline{\mathfrak{x}} - \overline{\mathfrak{y}}.$$

Theorem 263: *If*

$$\mathfrak{y} \neq \mathfrak{n}$$

then

$$\overline{\left(\frac{\mathfrak{x}}{\mathfrak{y}}\right)} = \frac{\overline{\mathfrak{x}}}{\overline{\mathfrak{y}}}.$$

Proof: Since

$$\mathfrak{x} = \frac{\mathfrak{x}}{\mathfrak{y}}\mathfrak{y},$$

we have, by Theorem 261, that

$$\overline{\mathfrak{x}} = \overline{\left(\frac{\mathfrak{x}}{\mathfrak{y}}\right)}\overline{\mathfrak{y}};$$

hence by Theorem 258, we have

$$\overline{\mathfrak{y}} \neq \mathfrak{n},$$

so that

$$\overline{\left(\frac{\mathfrak{x}}{\mathfrak{y}}\right)} = \frac{\overline{\mathfrak{x}}}{\overline{\mathfrak{y}}}.$$

§ 7

Absolute Value

Definition 66: *Denote by* $\sqrt{\zeta}$ *the* (positive) *solution* ξ *—whose existence and uniqueness was established by Theorem* 161*—of the equation*

$$\xi\xi = \zeta.$$

Definition 67:

$$\sqrt{0} = 0.$$

Definition 68:

$$|[\Xi_1, \Xi_2]| = \sqrt{\Xi_1 \Xi_1 + \Xi_2 \Xi_2}.$$

(| | to be read "absolute value," or "modulus.")

Theorem 264:

$$|\mathfrak{x}| \begin{cases} > 0 \text{ for } \mathfrak{x} \neq \mathfrak{n}, \\ = 0 \text{ for } \mathfrak{x} = \mathfrak{n}. \end{cases}$$

Proof: Definitions 68, 66, and 67.

Theorem 265:

$$|[\Xi_1, \Xi_2]| \geqq |\Xi_1|,$$
$$|[\Xi_1, \Xi_2]| \geqq |\Xi_2|.$$

Proof:

$$|[\Xi_1, \Xi_2]|\,|[\Xi_1, \Xi_2]|$$
$$= \Xi_1 \Xi_1 + \Xi_2 \Xi_2 \begin{cases} \geqq \Xi_1 \Xi_1 = |\Xi_1|\,|\Xi_1|, \\ \geqq \Xi_2 \Xi_2 = |\Xi_2|\,|\Xi_2|. \end{cases}$$

If

$$\Xi\Xi \geqq HH, \quad \Xi \geqq 0, \quad H \geqq 0$$

then

$$\Xi \geqq H,$$

since otherwise

$$0 < \Xi < H,$$
$$\Xi\Xi < HH$$

would follow. Thus Theorem 265 is proved.

Theorem 266: *If*

$$[\Xi, 0][\Xi, 0] = [H, 0][H, 0], \quad \Xi \geqq 0, \quad H \geqq 0$$

then

$$\Xi = H.$$

Proof: Since

$$[Z, 0]\,[Z, 0] = [ZZ - 0 \cdot 0, \; Z \cdot 0 + 0 \cdot Z] = [ZZ, 0],$$

the hypothesis gives

$$[\Xi\Xi, 0] = [HH, 0],$$
$$\Xi\Xi = HH.$$

If

$$\Xi > 0,$$

then

$$HH = \Xi\Xi > 0,$$

$$H > 0,$$

hence, by Theorem 161,

$$\Xi = H.$$

If

$$\Xi = 0,$$

then

$$HH = \Xi\Xi = 0,$$

$$H = 0 = \Xi.$$

Theorem 267: $[|\mathfrak{x}|, 0][|\mathfrak{x}|, 0] = \mathfrak{x}\bar{\mathfrak{x}}$.

Proof: If we set

$$\mathfrak{x} = [\Xi_1, \Xi_2],$$

then we have

$$[|\mathfrak{x}|, 0][|\mathfrak{x}|, 0] = [|\mathfrak{x}||\mathfrak{x}|, 0] = [\Xi_1\Xi_1 + \Xi_2\Xi_2, 0]$$
$$= [\Xi_1\Xi_1 - \Xi_2(-\Xi_2), \Xi_1(-\Xi_2) + \Xi_2\Xi_1] = [\Xi_1, \Xi_2][\Xi_1, -\Xi_2] = \mathfrak{x}\bar{\mathfrak{x}}.$$

Theorem 268: $|\mathfrak{x}\mathfrak{y}| = |\mathfrak{x}||\mathfrak{y}|$.

Proof: By Theorems 267 and 261, we have that

$$[|\mathfrak{x}\mathfrak{y}|, 0][|\mathfrak{x}\mathfrak{y}|, 0] = (\mathfrak{x}\mathfrak{y})\overline{\mathfrak{x}\mathfrak{y}} = (\mathfrak{x}\mathfrak{y})(\bar{\mathfrak{x}}\bar{\mathfrak{y}}) = (\mathfrak{x}\bar{\mathfrak{x}})(\mathfrak{y}\bar{\mathfrak{y}})$$
$$= ([|\mathfrak{x}|, 0][|\mathfrak{x}|, 0])([|\mathfrak{y}|, 0][|\mathfrak{y}|, 0])$$
$$= ([|\mathfrak{x}|, 0][|\mathfrak{y}|, 0])([|\mathfrak{x}|, 0][|\mathfrak{y}|, 0])$$
$$= [|\mathfrak{x}||\mathfrak{y}| - 0\cdot 0, |\mathfrak{x}|\cdot 0 + 0\cdot|\mathfrak{y}|][|\mathfrak{x}||\mathfrak{y}| - 0\cdot 0, |\mathfrak{x}|\cdot 0 + 0\cdot|\mathfrak{y}|]$$
$$= [|\mathfrak{x}||\mathfrak{y}|, 0][|\mathfrak{x}||\mathfrak{y}|, 0],$$

hence by Theorem 266 that

$$|\mathfrak{x}\mathfrak{y}| = |\mathfrak{x}||\mathfrak{y}|.$$

Theorem 269: *If*

$$\mathfrak{y} \neq \mathfrak{n},$$

then

$$\left|\frac{\mathfrak{x}}{\mathfrak{y}}\right| = \frac{|\mathfrak{x}|}{|\mathfrak{y}|}.$$

Proof:

$$|\mathfrak{y}| > 0,$$

$$\frac{\mathfrak{x}}{\mathfrak{y}}\mathfrak{y} = \mathfrak{x},$$

hence, by Theorem 268,

$$\left|\frac{\mathfrak{x}}{\mathfrak{y}}\right| |\mathfrak{y}| = |\mathfrak{x}|,$$

$$\left|\frac{\mathfrak{x}}{\mathfrak{y}}\right| = \frac{|\mathfrak{x}|}{|\mathfrak{y}|}.$$

Theorem 270: *If*

$$\mathfrak{x}+\mathfrak{y} = \mathfrak{e}$$

then

$$|\mathfrak{x}|+|\mathfrak{y}| \geqq 1.$$

Proof: If

$$\mathfrak{x} = [\Xi_1, \Xi\ ], \quad \mathfrak{y} = [H_1, H_2],$$

then Theorem 265 gives

$$|\mathfrak{x}| \geqq |\Xi_1| \geqq \Xi_1,$$

$$|\mathfrak{y}| \geqq |H_1| \geqq H_1,$$

hence

$$|\mathfrak{x}|+|\mathfrak{y}| \geqq \Xi_1 + H_1 = 1.$$

Theorem 271: $|\mathfrak{x}+\mathfrak{y}| \leqq |\mathfrak{x}|+|\mathfrak{y}|$.

Proof: 1) If

$$\mathfrak{x}+\mathfrak{y} = \mathfrak{n},$$

then the left-hand side of the inequality is 0, hence $\leqq$ the right-hand side.

2) If

$$\mathfrak{x}+\mathfrak{y} \neq \mathfrak{n},$$

then, since

$$\frac{\mathfrak{x}}{\mathfrak{x}+\mathfrak{y}} + \frac{\mathfrak{y}}{\mathfrak{x}+\mathfrak{y}} = \frac{\mathfrak{x}+\mathfrak{y}}{\mathfrak{x}+\mathfrak{y}} = \mathfrak{e},$$

Theorem 270 gives

$$\left|\frac{\mathfrak{x}}{\mathfrak{x}+\mathfrak{y}}\right| + \left|\frac{\mathfrak{y}}{\mathfrak{x}+\mathfrak{y}}\right| \geqq 1,$$

so that, by Theorem 269,

$$\frac{|\mathfrak{x}|}{|\mathfrak{x}+\mathfrak{y}|} + \frac{|\mathfrak{y}|}{|\mathfrak{x}+\mathfrak{y}|} \geqq 1,$$

$$|\mathfrak{x}|+|\mathfrak{y}| = |\mathfrak{x}+\mathfrak{y}|\left(\frac{|\mathfrak{x}|}{|\mathfrak{x}+\mathfrak{y}|} + \frac{|\mathfrak{y}|}{|\mathfrak{x}+\mathfrak{y}|}\right) \geqq |\mathfrak{x}+\mathfrak{y}|.$$

Theorem 272: $|-\mathfrak{x}| = |\mathfrak{x}|$.

Proof: $(-\Xi_1)(-\Xi_1)+(-\Xi_2)(-\Xi_2) = \Xi_1\Xi_1 + \Xi_2\Xi_2$.

Theorem 273: $|\mathfrak{x}-\mathfrak{y}| \geqq \big||\mathfrak{x}|-|\mathfrak{y}|\big|$.

Proof: $\mathfrak{x} = \mathfrak{y}+(\mathfrak{x}-\mathfrak{y})$,

hence, by Theorem 271,

$$|\mathfrak{x}| \leqq |\mathfrak{y}| + |\mathfrak{x}-\mathfrak{y}|,$$
$$|\mathfrak{x}-\mathfrak{y}| \geqq |\mathfrak{x}| - |\mathfrak{y}|.$$

From this we obtain, by interchanging $\mathfrak{x}$ and $\mathfrak{y}$, that

$$|\mathfrak{y}-\mathfrak{x}| \geqq |\mathfrak{y}| - |\mathfrak{x}|,$$

so that, by Theorem 272,

$$|\mathfrak{x}-\mathfrak{y}| = |-(\mathfrak{y}-\mathfrak{x})| = |\mathfrak{y}-\mathfrak{x}| \geqq |\mathfrak{y}| - |\mathfrak{x}| = -(|\mathfrak{x}| - |\mathfrak{y}|).$$

But

$$\Xi \geqq H, \quad \Xi \geqq -H$$

implies, since $|H|$ is equal either to H or to $-H$, that

$$\Xi \geqq |H|.$$

Therefore we obtain

$$|\mathfrak{x}-\mathfrak{y}| \geqq \big||\mathfrak{x}| - |\mathfrak{y}|\big|.$$

§ 8

Sums and Products

Theorem 274: *If*

$$x < y,$$

then the $m \leqq x$ *and the* $n \leqq y$ *can not be put into one-to-one correspondence.*

Throughout this section, I will use the term "correspondence" to mean "one-to-one correspondence."

Proof: Let $\mathfrak{M}$ be the set of all x with the property that the assertion holds for all $y > x$.

I) If

$$1 < y,$$

then we can not set up a correspondence between $m = 1$ and the $n \leqq y$. For if to $m = 1$ there corresponds $n = 1$, then there does not remain any m to correspond to $n = y$; and if to $m = 1$ there corresponds an $n > 1$, then there does not remain any m to correspond to $n = 1$.

Hence 1 belongs to $\mathfrak{M}$.

II) Let x belong to $\mathfrak{M}$, and let

$$x + 1 < y.$$

Assuming we had a correspondence between the $m \leqq x + 1$ and the $n \leqq y$, we distinguish two cases as follows:

α) To $m = x + 1$ corresponds $n = y$. Then the $m \leqq x$ must correspond to the $n \leqq y - 1$; but this is impossible, since

$$x < y - 1.$$

β) To $m = x + 1$ corresponds an $n = n_0 < y$. Then let $m = m_0$ be the number corresponding to $n = y$, so that $m_0 < x + 1$. Consider now the following modified correspondence between the $m \leqq x + 1$ and the $n \leqq y$:

$$\begin{cases} \text{For } m \neq m_0,\ m \neq x + 1, \text{ preserve the status quo.} \\ \text{Let } m = m_0 \text{ correspond to } n = n_0. \\ \text{Let } m = x + 1 \text{ correspond to } n = y. \end{cases}$$

This gives a correspondence of the sort whose impossibility we have just established in α) above.

Hence $x + 1$ belongs to $\mathfrak{M}$, and the assertion is proved.

Since the proofs of Theorems 275 through 278, and 280 through 286 below, as well as the corresponding definitions, would be word for word the same in the case of sums as in the case of products, we will avoid lengthy repetitions by doing everything just once. For this, we choose a neutral symbol $\dotplus$ which is to stand for $+$ throughout, or for $\cdot$ throughout. We introduce another symbol, Ξ, which will be neutral for the time being but which will later be split into two symbols ($\sum$ in the case of $+$, $\prod$ in the case of $\cdot$) —By "defined" I will mean, in what follows, "defined as a complex number."

Theorem 275: *Let x be fixed, and let $\mathfrak{f}(n)$ be defined for $n \leqq x$. Then there exists exactly one*

$$\mathfrak{g}_x(n)$$

defined for all $n \leqq x$ (and written more fully as

$$\mathfrak{g}_{x,\mathfrak{f}}(n),$$

more briefly as

$$\mathfrak{g}(n))$$

with the following properties:

$$\mathfrak{g}_x(1) = \mathfrak{f}(1),$$

$$\mathfrak{g}_x(n+1) = \mathfrak{g}_x(n) \dotplus \mathfrak{f}(n+1) \textit{ for } n < x.$$

Proof: 1) We will show first that there is at most one such $\mathfrak{g}_x(n)$.

Let both $\mathfrak{g}(n)$ and $\mathfrak{h}(n)$ have the required properties. Let $\mathfrak{M}$ be the set which contains all those $n \leqq x$ for which

$$\mathfrak{g}(n) = \mathfrak{h}(n),$$

and all $n > x$ as well.

I) $$\mathfrak{g}(1) = \mathfrak{f}(1) = \mathfrak{h}(1);$$

hence 1 belongs to $\mathfrak{M}$.

II) Let n belong to $\mathfrak{M}$. Then either

$$n < x, \ \mathfrak{g}(n) = \mathfrak{h}(n),$$

hence

$$\mathfrak{g}(n+1) = \mathfrak{g}(n) \dotplus \mathfrak{f}(n+1) = \mathfrak{h}(n) \dotplus \mathfrak{f}(n+1) = \mathfrak{h}(n+1),$$

so that $n+1$ belongs to $\mathfrak{M}$;

or

$$n \geqq x,$$

hence

$$n+1 > x$$

so that, once more, $n+1$ belongs to $\mathfrak{M}$.

Therefore $\mathfrak{M}$ is the set of all positive integers, so that we have for every $n \leqq x$ that

$$\mathfrak{g}(n) = \mathfrak{h}(n),$$

as was to be proved.

2) Next we will show for any given x that if $\mathfrak{f}(n)$ is defined for every $n \leqq x$, then there does exist a suitable $\mathfrak{g}_x(n)$.

Let $\mathfrak{M}$ be the set of all x for which this holds, i.e. for which, $\mathfrak{f}(n)$ being defined for $n \leqq x$, there exists a suitable $\mathfrak{g}_x(n)$ (hence exactly one, by 1) above).

I) For $x = 1$, and assuming that $\mathfrak{f}(1)$ is defined, we have in

$$\mathfrak{g}_x(1) = \mathfrak{f}(1)$$

what is required (since the second of the properties stipulated in Theorem 275 is a vacuous requirement here, $n < 1$ being impossible). Hence 1 belongs to $\mathfrak{M}$.

II) Let x belong to $\mathfrak{M}$. If $\mathfrak{f}(n)$ is defined for $n \leqq x + 1$ then it is certainly defined for $n \leqq x$, so that for $n \leqq x$ there exists exactly one $\mathfrak{g}_x(n)$ associated with the $\mathfrak{f}(n)$. Now

$$\mathfrak{g}_{x+1}(n) = \begin{cases} \mathfrak{g}_x(n) \text{ for } n \leqq x, \\ \mathfrak{g}_x(x) \mathbin{+\!\!\!\!\div} \mathfrak{f}(x+1) \text{ for } n = x+1 \end{cases}$$

is as required for $x + 1$. For, we have firstly

$$\mathfrak{g}_{x+1}(1) = \mathfrak{g}_x(1) = \mathfrak{f}(1).$$

Secondly, for

$$n < x$$

we have (since $n + 1 \leqq x$) that

$$\mathfrak{g}_{x+1}(n+1) = \mathfrak{g}_x(n+1) = \mathfrak{g}_x(n) \mathbin{+\!\!\!\!\div} \mathfrak{f}(n+1) = \mathfrak{g}_{x+1}(n) \mathbin{+\!\!\!\!\div} \mathfrak{f}(n+1),$$

while if

$$n = x$$

then

$$\mathfrak{g}_{x+1}(n+1) = \mathfrak{g}_x(x) \mathbin{+\!\!\!\!\div} \mathfrak{f}(x+1) = \mathfrak{g}_{x+1}(n) \mathbin{+\!\!\!\!\div} \mathfrak{f}(n+1);$$

thus

$$n < x + 1$$

implies, in any case, that

$$\mathfrak{g}_{x+1}(n+1) = \mathfrak{g}_{x+1}(n) \mathbin{+\!\!\!\!\div} \mathfrak{f}(n+1).$$

Therefore $x + 1$ belongs to $\mathfrak{M}$, and $\mathfrak{M}$ contains all positive integers.

Theorem 276: *If $\mathfrak{f}(n)$ is defined for $n \leqq x + 1$, then we have for the associated $\mathfrak{g}_x(n)$ and $\mathfrak{g}_{x+1}(n)$ that*

$$\mathfrak{g}_{x+1}(x+1) = \mathfrak{g}_x(x) \mathbin{+\!\!\!\!\div} \mathfrak{f}(x+1).$$

Proof: This was observed in the construction in 2), II) of the preceding proof.

Definition 69: *If* $\mathfrak{f}(n)$ *is defined for* $n \leqq x$, *then*

$$\mathop{\mathfrak{S}}_{n=1}^{x} \mathfrak{f}(n) = \mathfrak{g}_x(x) \quad (= \mathfrak{g}_{x,\mathfrak{f}}(x)).$$

If $\mathbin{\overset{\cdot}{\underset{\cdot}{+}}}$ *signifies* $+$, *we write*

$$\sum_{n=1}^{x} \mathfrak{f}(n);$$

if $\mathbin{\overset{\cdot}{\underset{\cdot}{+}}}$ *signifies* $\cdot$, *we write*

$$\prod_{n=1}^{x} \mathfrak{f}(n).$$

(Σ to be read "sum"; Π to be read "product.")

In these symbols, we may use in place of n any other letter which stands for integers.

Theorem 277: *If* $\mathfrak{f}(1)$ *is defined, then*

$$\mathop{\mathfrak{S}}_{n=1}^{1} \mathfrak{f}(n) = \mathfrak{f}(1).$$

Proof:

$$\mathfrak{g}_1(1) = \mathfrak{f}(1).$$

Theorem 278: *If* $\mathfrak{f}(n)$ *is defined for* $n \leqq x+1$, *then*

$$\mathop{\mathfrak{S}}_{n=1}^{x+1} \mathfrak{f}(n) = \mathop{\mathfrak{S}}_{n=1}^{x} \mathfrak{f}(n) \mathbin{\overset{\cdot}{\underset{\cdot}{+}}} \mathfrak{f}(x+1).$$

Proof: Theorem 276.

Theorem 279:

$$\sum_{n=1}^{x} \mathfrak{x} = \mathfrak{x}[x, 0].$$

Proof: Fix $\mathfrak{x}$, and let $\mathfrak{M}$ be the set of all x for which this holds.

I) By Theorem 277, we have

$$\sum_{n=1}^{1} \mathfrak{x} = \mathfrak{x} = \mathfrak{x}\mathfrak{e} = \mathfrak{x}[1, 0].$$

Hence 1 belongs to $\mathfrak{M}$.

II) If x belongs to $\mathfrak{M}$, then we have by Theorem 278 that

$$\sum_{n=1}^{x+1} \mathfrak{x} = \sum_{n=1}^{x} \mathfrak{x} + \mathfrak{x} = \mathfrak{x}[x, 0] + \mathfrak{x}[1, 0] = \mathfrak{x}([x, 0] + [1, 0])$$
$$= \mathfrak{x}[x+1, 0].$$

Hence $x+1$ belongs to $\mathfrak{M}$.

Therefore the assertion holds for all x.

Theorem 280: *If* $\mathfrak{f}(1)$ *and* $\mathfrak{f}(1+1)$ *are defined, then*

$$\sum_{n=1}^{1+1} \mathfrak{f}(n) = \mathfrak{f}(1) \dotplus \mathfrak{f}(1+1).$$

Proof: By Theorems 278 and 277, we have

$$\sum_{n=1}^{1+1} \mathfrak{f}(n) = \sum_{n=1}^{1} \mathfrak{f}(n) \dotplus \mathfrak{f}(1+1) = \mathfrak{f}(1) \dotplus \mathfrak{f}(1+1).$$

Theorem 281: *If* $\mathfrak{f}(n)$ *is defined for* $n \leqq x+y$, *then*

$$\sum_{n=1}^{x+y} \mathfrak{f}(n) = \sum_{n=1}^{x} \mathfrak{f}(n) \dotplus \sum_{n=1}^{y} \mathfrak{f}(x+n).$$

Proof: Fix x, and let $\mathfrak{M}$ be the set of all y for which this holds.

I) If $\mathfrak{f}(n)$ is defined for $n \leqq x+1$, then we have by Theorems 278 and 277 that

$$\sum_{n=1}^{x+1} \mathfrak{f}(n) = \sum_{n=1}^{x} \mathfrak{f}(n) \dotplus \mathfrak{f}(x+1) = \sum_{n=1}^{x} \mathfrak{f}(n) \dotplus \sum_{n=1}^{1} \mathfrak{f}(x+n).$$

Hence 1 belongs to $\mathfrak{M}$.

II) Let y belong to $\mathfrak{M}$. If $\mathfrak{f}(n)$ is defined for $n \leqq x+(y+1)$, then we have by Theorem 278 (applied to $x+y$ instead of x) that

$$\sum_{n=1}^{x+(y+1)} \mathfrak{f}(n) = \sum_{n=1}^{(x+y)+1} \mathfrak{f}(n) = \sum_{n=1}^{x+y} \mathfrak{f}(n) \dotplus \mathfrak{f}((x+y)+1)$$

$$= \left(\sum_{n=1}^{x} \mathfrak{f}(n) \dotplus \sum_{n=1}^{y} \mathfrak{f}(x+n)\right) \dotplus \mathfrak{f}(x+(y+1))$$

$$= \sum_{n=1}^{x} \mathfrak{f}(n) \dotplus \left(\sum_{n=1}^{y} \mathfrak{f}(x+n) \dotplus \mathfrak{f}(x+(y+1))\right),$$

which by Theorem 278 (applied to y instead of x, and to $\mathfrak{f}(x+n)$ instead of $\mathfrak{f}(n)$) is

$$= \sum_{n=1}^{x} \mathfrak{f}(n) \dotplus \sum_{n=1}^{y+1} \mathfrak{f}(x+n).$$

Hence $y+1$ belongs to $\mathfrak{M}$, and Theorem 281 is proved.

Theorem 282: *If* $\mathfrak{f}(n)$ *and* $\mathfrak{g}(n)$ *are defined for* $n \leqq x$, *then*

$$\sum_{n=1}^{x} (\mathfrak{f}(n) \dotplus \mathfrak{g}(n)) = \sum_{n=1}^{x} \mathfrak{f}(n) \dotplus \sum_{n=1}^{x} \mathfrak{g}(n).$$

Proof: Let $\mathfrak{M}$ be the set of all x for which this holds.

I) If $\mathfrak{f}(1)$ and $\mathfrak{g}(1)$ are defined, then

$$\sum_{n=1}^{1} (\mathfrak{f}(n) \dotplus \mathfrak{g}(n)) = \mathfrak{f}(1) \dotplus \mathfrak{g}(1) = \sum_{n=1}^{1} \mathfrak{f}(n) \dotplus \sum_{n=1}^{1} \mathfrak{g}(n).$$

Hence 1 belongs to $\mathfrak{M}$.

II) Let x belong to $\mathfrak{M}$. If $\mathfrak{f}(n)$ and $\mathfrak{g}(n)$ are defined for $n \leqq x + 1$, then we have, since

$$(\mathfrak{x} \dotplus \mathfrak{y}) \dotplus (\mathfrak{z} \dotplus \mathfrak{u}) = ((\mathfrak{x} \dotplus \mathfrak{y}) \dotplus \mathfrak{z}) \dotplus \mathfrak{u} = (\mathfrak{z} \dotplus (\mathfrak{x} \dotplus \mathfrak{y})) \dotplus \mathfrak{u}$$
$$= ((\mathfrak{z} \dotplus \mathfrak{x}) \dotplus \mathfrak{y}) \dotplus \mathfrak{u} = (\mathfrak{z} \dotplus \mathfrak{x}) \dotplus (\mathfrak{y} \dotplus \mathfrak{u}) = (\mathfrak{x} \dotplus \mathfrak{z}) \dotplus (\mathfrak{y} \dotplus \mathfrak{u}),$$

$$\mathop{\mathfrak{S}}_{n=1}^{x+1} (\mathfrak{f}(n) \dotplus \mathfrak{g}(n)) = \mathop{\mathfrak{S}}_{n=1}^{x} (\mathfrak{f}(n) \dotplus \mathfrak{g}(n)) \dotplus (\mathfrak{f}(x+1) \dotplus \mathfrak{g}(x+1))$$
$$= \left(\mathop{\mathfrak{S}}_{n=1}^{x} \mathfrak{f}(n) \dotplus \mathop{\mathfrak{S}}_{n=1}^{x} \mathfrak{g}(n)\right) \dotplus (\mathfrak{f}(x+1) \dotplus \mathfrak{g}(x+1))$$
$$= \left(\mathop{\mathfrak{S}}_{n=1}^{x} \mathfrak{f}(n) \dotplus \mathfrak{f}(x+1)\right) \dotplus \left(\mathop{\mathfrak{S}}_{n=1}^{x} \mathfrak{g}(n) \dotplus \mathfrak{g}(x+1)\right)$$
$$= \mathop{\mathfrak{S}}_{n=1}^{x+1} \mathfrak{f}(n) \dotplus \mathop{\mathfrak{S}}_{n=1}^{x+1} \mathfrak{g}(n).$$

Hence $x + 1$ belongs to $\mathfrak{M}$, and the assertion holds for all x.

Theorem 283: *Let $s(n)$ set up a correspondence between the $n \leqq x$ and the $m \leqq x$. Let $\mathfrak{f}(n)$ be defined for $n \leqq x$. Then*

$$\mathop{\mathfrak{S}}_{n=1}^{x} \mathfrak{f}(s(n)) = \mathop{\mathfrak{S}}_{n=1}^{x} \mathfrak{f}(n).$$

Proof: We set

$$\mathfrak{f}(s(n)) = \mathfrak{g}(n)$$

as an abbreviation.

Denote by $\mathfrak{M}$ the set of all x for which the assertion

$$\mathop{\mathfrak{S}}_{n=1}^{x} \mathfrak{g}(n) = \mathop{\mathfrak{S}}_{n=1}^{x} \mathfrak{f}(n)$$

holds (for all admissible s and $\mathfrak{f}$).

I) If

$$x = 1$$

then

$$s(1) = 1,$$

hence, if $\mathfrak{f}(1)$ is defined,

$$\mathop{\mathfrak{S}}_{n=1}^{x} \mathfrak{g}(n) = \mathfrak{g}(1) = \mathfrak{f}(1) = \mathop{\mathfrak{S}}_{n=1}^{x} \mathfrak{f}(n).$$

Therefore 1 belongs to $\mathfrak{M}$.

II) Let x belong to $\mathfrak{M}$. Let $s(n)$ set up a correspondence between the $n \leqq x + 1$ and the $m \leqq x + 1$, and let $\mathfrak{f}(n)$ be defined for $n \leqq x + 1$.

1) If $$s(x + 1) = x + 1,$$

then $s(n)$ makes the $n \leqq x$ correspond to the $m \leqq x$, so that we have

$$\sum_{n=1}^{x} \mathfrak{g}(n) = \sum_{n=1}^{x} \mathfrak{f}(n),$$

$$\mathfrak{g}(x+1) = \mathfrak{f}(x+1),$$

hence

$$\sum_{n=1}^{x+1} \mathfrak{g}(n) = \sum_{n=1}^{x} \mathfrak{g}(n) \dotplus \mathfrak{g}(x+1) = \sum_{n=1}^{x} \mathfrak{f}(n) \dotplus \mathfrak{f}(x+1) = \sum_{n=1}^{x+1} \mathfrak{f}(n)$$

2) If

$$s(x+1) < x+1, \quad s(1) = 1,$$

then $s(n)$ makes the n for which $1 + 1 \leqq n \leqq x + 1$ correspond to the m for which $1 + 1 \leqq m \leqq x + 1$; hence $s(1 + n) - 1$ makes the $n \leqq x$ correspond to the $m \leqq x$. Therefore we have

$$\sum_{n=1}^{x} \mathfrak{g}(1+n) = \sum_{n=1}^{x} \mathfrak{f}(s(1+n)) = \sum_{n=1}^{x} \mathfrak{f}(1+(s(1+n)-1))$$

$$= \sum_{n=1}^{x} \mathfrak{f}(1+n),$$

hence, by Theorem 281,

$$\sum_{n=1}^{x+1} \mathfrak{g}(n) = \mathfrak{g}(1) \dotplus \sum_{n=1}^{x} \mathfrak{g}(1+n) = \mathfrak{f}(1) \dotplus \sum_{n=1}^{x} \mathfrak{f}(1+n) = \sum_{n=1}^{x+1} \mathfrak{f}(n)$$

3) If

$$s(x+1) < x+1, \; s(1) > 1,$$

set

$$s(1) = a$$

and determine b from

$$1 \leqq b \leqq x+1, \quad s(b) = 1.$$

Then we have

$$a > 1, \; b > 1.$$

α) Let

$$a < x+1.$$

Then each of

$$s_1(n) = \begin{cases} 1 & \text{for } n = 1, \\ a & \text{for } n = b, \\ s(n) & \text{for } 1 < n \leqq x+1, \; n \neq b \end{cases}$$

and

$$s_2(n) = \begin{cases} a & \text{for } n = 1, \\ 1 & \text{for } n = a, \\ n & \text{for } 1 < n \leqq x+1, \; n \neq a \end{cases}$$

makes the $n \leqq x + 1$ correspond to the $m \leqq x + 1$.

Now we have

$$s(n) = s_2(s_1(n)) \text{ for } n \leqq x+1.$$

For, by means of $s_2(s_1(n))$

1 is first sent into 1 and from there into $a = s(1)$,
b is first sent into a and from there into $1 = s(b)$,
every other $n \leqq x+1$ is first sent into $s(n)$, thence into $s(n)$.

$s_1(n)$ leaves 1 unchanged, and $s_2(n)$ leaves $x+1$ unchanged. We therefore have by 1) and 2) that

$$\sum_{n=1}^{x+1} \mathfrak{g}(n) = \sum_{n=1}^{x+1} \mathfrak{f}(s(n)) = \sum_{n=1}^{x+1} \mathfrak{f}(s_2(s_1(n))) = \sum_{n=1}^{x+1} \mathfrak{f}(s_2(n)) = \sum_{n=1}^{x+1} \mathfrak{f}(n).$$

β) Let

$$a = x+1, \quad b < x+1.$$

Then

$$s_3(n) = \begin{cases} b \text{ for } n = 1, \\ 1 \text{ for } n = b, \\ n \text{ for } 1 < n \leqq x+1, \ n \neq b \end{cases}$$

makes the $n \leqq x+1$ correspond to the $m \leqq x+1$. Moreover

$$s(n) = s_1(s_3(n)) \text{ for } n \leqq x+1.$$

For, by means of $s_1(s_3(n))$

1 is first sent into b and from there into $a = s(1)$,
b is first sent into 1 and from there into $1 = s(b)$,
every other $n \leqq x+1$ is first sent into n, thence into $s(n)$.

$s_3(n)$ leaves $x+1$ unchanged. We therefore have by 1) and 2) that

$$\sum_{n=1}^{x+1} \mathfrak{g}(n) = \sum_{n=1}^{x+1} \mathfrak{f}(s(n)) = \sum_{n=1}^{x+1} \mathfrak{f}(s_1(s_3(n))) = \sum_{n=1}^{x+1} \mathfrak{f}(s_1(n)) = \sum_{n=1}^{x+1} \mathfrak{f}(n).$$

γ) Let

$$a = b = x+1.$$

If $x = 1$, then

$$\sum_{n=1}^{x+1} \mathfrak{g}(n) = \sum_{n=1}^{x+1} \mathfrak{f}(n)$$

is trivial.

If $x > 1$, then by

$$s_4(n) = \begin{cases} 1 \text{ for } n = 1, \\ x+1 \text{ for } n = x+1, \\ s(n) \text{ for } 1 < n < x+1, \end{cases}$$

the $n \leqq x+1$ are made to correspond to the $m \leqq x+1$. Hence, by 1),

$$\sum_{n=1}^{x+1} \mathfrak{g}(n) = \sum_{n=1}^{x} \mathfrak{g}(n) \mathbin{+\!\!\!\!\cdot\cdot} \mathfrak{g}(x+1) = \left(\mathfrak{g}(1) \mathbin{+\!\!\!\!\cdot\cdot} \sum_{n=1}^{x-1} \mathfrak{g}(n+1)\right) \mathbin{+\!\!\!\!\cdot\cdot} \mathfrak{g}(x+1)$$

$$= \mathfrak{g}(1) \mathbin{+\!\!\!\!\cdot\cdot} \left(\sum_{n=1}^{x-1} \mathfrak{g}(n+1) \mathbin{+\!\!\!\!\cdot\cdot} \mathfrak{g}(x+1)\right)$$

$$= \left(\mathfrak{g}(x+1) \mathbin{+\!\!\!\!\cdot\cdot} \sum_{n=1}^{x-1} \mathfrak{g}(n+1)\right) \mathbin{+\!\!\!\!\cdot\cdot} \mathfrak{g}(1)$$

$$= \left(\mathfrak{f}(s(x+1)) \mathbin{+\!\!\!\!\cdot\cdot} \sum_{n=1}^{x-1} \mathfrak{f}(s(n+1))\right) \mathbin{+\!\!\!\!\cdot\cdot} \mathfrak{f}(s(1))$$

$$= \left(\mathfrak{f}(1) \mathbin{+\!\!\!\!\cdot\cdot} \sum_{n=1}^{x-1} \mathfrak{f}(s_4(n+1))\right) \mathbin{+\!\!\!\!\cdot\cdot} \mathfrak{f}(x+1)$$

$$= \left(\mathfrak{f}(s_4(1)) \mathbin{+\!\!\!\!\cdot\cdot} \sum_{n=1}^{x-1} \mathfrak{f}(s_4(n+1))\right) \mathbin{+\!\!\!\!\cdot\cdot} \mathfrak{f}(s_4(x+1))$$

$$= \sum_{n=1}^{x} \mathfrak{f}(s_4(n)) \mathbin{+\!\!\!\!\cdot\cdot} \mathfrak{f}(s_4(x+1)) = \sum_{n=1}^{x+1} \mathfrak{f}(s_4(n)) = \sum_{n=1}^{x+1} \mathfrak{f}(n).$$

Therefore $x+1$ belongs to $\mathfrak{M}$, and the Theorem is proved.

In Definition 70 and in Theorems 284 through 286, we will, as an exception, let small italic letters stand for any (not necessarily positive) integers.

Definition 70: *Let*

$$y \leqq x,$$

and let $\mathfrak{f}(n)$ *be defined for*

$$y \leqq n \leqq x.$$

Then

$$\sum_{n=y}^{x} \mathfrak{f}(n) = \sum_{n=1}^{(x+1)-y} \mathfrak{f}((n+y)-1).$$

Here we could use, instead of n, any other letter which stands for integers.

Note that

$$x+1 > y;\ y \leqq (n+y)-1 \leqq x \text{ for } 1 \leqq n \leqq (x+1)-y;$$

note also that for $y = 1$, Definition 70 agrees (as it should) with Definition 69.

Theorem 284: *Let*

$$y \leqq u < x;$$

let $\mathfrak{f}(n)$ *be defined for*

$$y \leqq n \leqq x.$$

Then

$$\overset{x}{\underset{n=y}{\mathsf{Z}}}\, \mathfrak{f}(n) = \overset{u}{\underset{n=y}{\mathsf{Z}}}\, \mathfrak{f}(n) \divideontimes \overset{x}{\underset{n=u+1}{\mathsf{Z}}}\, \mathfrak{f}(n).$$

Proof: By Definition 70 and Theorem 281, we have

$$\overset{x}{\underset{n=y}{\mathsf{Z}}}\, \mathfrak{f}(n) = \overset{(x+1)-y}{\underset{n=1}{\mathsf{Z}}}\, \mathfrak{f}((n+y)-1)$$

$$= \overset{(u+1)-y}{\underset{n=1}{\mathsf{Z}}}\, \mathfrak{f}((n+y)-1) \divideontimes \overset{x-u}{\underset{n=1}{\mathsf{Z}}}\, \mathfrak{f}(((((u+1)-y)+n)+y)-1),$$

since

$$((u+1)-y)+(x-u) = (x+(-u))+((u+1)+(-y))$$
$$= (x+((-u)+(u+1)))+(-y) = (x+1)-y.$$

Now we have

$$(((u+1)-y)+n)+y = ((u+1)-y)+(y+n)$$
$$= (((u+1)-y)+y)+n = n+(u+1),$$

so that, by Definition 70,

$$\overset{x}{\underset{n=y}{\mathsf{Z}}}\, \mathfrak{f}(n) = \overset{u}{\underset{n=y}{\mathsf{Z}}}\, \mathfrak{f}(n) \divideontimes \overset{(x+1)-(u+1)}{\underset{n=1}{\mathsf{Z}}}\, \mathfrak{f}((n+(u+1))-1)$$

$$= \overset{u}{\underset{n=y}{\mathsf{Z}}}\, \mathfrak{f}(n) \divideontimes \overset{x}{\underset{n=u+1}{\mathsf{Z}}}\, \mathfrak{f}(n).$$

Theorem 285: *Let*

$$y \leqq x,$$

and let $\mathfrak{f}(n)$ *be defined for*

$$y \leqq n \leqq x.$$

Then

$$\overset{x}{\underset{n=y}{\mathsf{Z}}}\, \mathfrak{f}(n) = \overset{x+v}{\underset{n=y+v}{\mathsf{Z}}}\, \mathfrak{f}(n-v).$$

Proof: By Definition 70, the left-hand side of this equality is

$$= \overset{(x+1)-y}{\underset{n=1}{\mathsf{Z}}}\, \mathfrak{f}((n+y)-1),$$

while the right-hand side (note: $y \leqq n-v \leqq x$ for $y+v \leqq n \leqq x+v$) is

$$= \overset{((x+v)+1)-(y+v)}{\underset{n=1}{\mathsf{Z}}}\, \mathfrak{f}(((n+(y+v))-1)-v);$$

in this, we have

$$((x+v)+1)-(y+v) = (1+(x+v))+((-v)+(-y))$$
$$= (1+((x+v)+(-v)))+(-y) = (1+x)-y = (x+1)-y$$

and

$$((n+(y+v))-1)-v = (n+(y+v))-(1+v) = ((n+y)+v)+(-v+(-1))$$
$$= (((n+y)+v)+(-v))+(-1) = ((n+y)+(v+(-v)))-1 = (n+y)-1.$$

Theorem 286: *Let $y \leqq x$ and let $\mathfrak{f}(n)$ be defined for*

$$y \leqq n \leqq x.$$

Let $s(n)$ establish a correspondence between the n for which $y \leqq n \leqq x$ and the m for which $y \leqq m \leqq x$. Then

$$\sum_{n=y}^{x} \mathfrak{f}(s(n)) = \sum_{n=y}^{x} \mathfrak{f}(n).$$

Proof:
$$s_1(n) = s((n+y)-1)-(y-1)$$

sets up a correspondence between the positive $n \leqq (x+1)-y$ and the positive $m \leqq (x+1)-y$. Hence, by Theorem 283,

$$\sum_{n=y}^{x} \mathfrak{f}(s(n)) = \sum_{n=1}^{(x+1)-y} \mathfrak{f}(s((n+y)-1)) = \sum_{n=1}^{(x+1)-y} \mathfrak{f}(s_1(n)+(y-1))$$
$$= \sum_{n=1}^{(x+1)-y} \mathfrak{f}(n+(y-1)) = \sum_{n=1}^{(x+1)-y} \mathfrak{f}((n+y)-1) = \sum_{n=y}^{x} \mathfrak{f}(n).$$

In place of

$$\sum_{n=y}^{x} \mathfrak{f}(n),$$

the sloppier notation

$$\mathfrak{f}(y)+\mathfrak{f}(y+1)+\cdots+\mathfrak{f}(x)$$

is also used (and a similar one for products); but an entirely unobjectionable notation is, for instance,

$$\mathfrak{f}(1)+\mathfrak{f}(1+1)+\mathfrak{f}((1+1)+1)+\mathfrak{f}(((1+1)+1)+1),$$

in other words,

$$\mathfrak{a}+\mathfrak{b}+\mathfrak{c}+\mathfrak{d}$$

—which, by definition, goes back to the earlier concept of addition, and means

$$((\mathfrak{a}+\mathfrak{b})+\mathfrak{c})+\mathfrak{d},$$

—or, for instance,

$$\mathfrak{a}\,\mathfrak{b}\,\mathfrak{c}\,\mathfrak{d}\,\mathfrak{f}\,\mathfrak{g}\,\mathfrak{h}\,\mathfrak{i}\,\mathfrak{k}\,\mathfrak{l}\,\mathfrak{m}\,\mathfrak{o}\,\mathfrak{p}\,\mathfrak{q}\,\mathfrak{r}\,\mathfrak{s}\,\mathfrak{t}\,\mathfrak{u}\,\mathfrak{v}\,\mathfrak{w}\,\mathfrak{x}\,\mathfrak{y}\,\mathfrak{z}.$$

Nor need we hesitate to write, for instance,

$$\mathfrak{a} - \mathfrak{b} + \mathfrak{c}$$

to mean

$$\mathfrak{a} + (-\mathfrak{b}) + \mathfrak{c},$$

since what is meant is

$$\mathfrak{f}(1) + \mathfrak{f}(1+1) + \mathfrak{f}((1+1)+1),$$

with

$$\mathfrak{f}(1) = \mathfrak{a}, \quad \mathfrak{f}(1+1) = -\mathfrak{b}, \quad \mathfrak{f}((1+1)+1) = \mathfrak{c}.$$

For the remainder of this section, small italic letters will again stand for positive integers.

Theorem 287: *If $\mathfrak{f}(n)$ is defined for $n \leqq x$, then there exists a Ξ such that*

$$\left|\sum_{n=1}^{x} \mathfrak{f}(n)\right| \leqq \Xi,$$

$$\sum_{n=1}^{x} [|\mathfrak{f}(n)|, 0] = [\Xi, 0].$$

Proof: Let $\mathfrak{M}$ be the set of all x for which (with $\mathfrak{f}(n)$ arbitrary) there exists such a Ξ.

I) If $\mathfrak{f}(1)$ is defined, then

$$\left|\sum_{n=1}^{1} \mathfrak{f}(n)\right| = |\mathfrak{f}(1)|,$$

$$\sum_{n=1}^{1} [|\mathfrak{f}(n)|, 0] = [|\mathfrak{f}(1)|, 0];$$

hence

$$\Xi = |\mathfrak{f}(1)|$$

is as required for $x = 1$. Therefore 1 belongs to $\mathfrak{M}$.

II) Let x belong to $\mathfrak{M}$. If $\mathfrak{f}(n)$ is defined for $n \leqq x + 1$, then there exists a Ξ_1 such that

$$\left|\sum_{n=1}^{x} \mathfrak{f}(n)\right| \leqq \Xi_1,$$

$$\sum_{n=1}^{x} [|\mathfrak{f}(n)|, 0] = [\Xi_1, 0].$$

By Theorems 278 and 271, we have that

$$\left|\sum_{n=1}^{x+1} \mathfrak{f}(n)\right| = \left|\sum_{n=1}^{x} \mathfrak{f}(n) + \mathfrak{f}(x+1)\right| \leqq \left|\sum_{n=1}^{x} \mathfrak{f}(n)\right| + |\mathfrak{f}(x+1)|$$
$$\leqq \Xi_1 + |\mathfrak{f}(x+1)|,$$

hence, setting

$$\Xi = \Xi_1 + |\mathfrak{f}(x+1)|,$$

that

$$\left|\sum_{n=1}^{x+1} \mathfrak{f}(n)\right| \leqq \Xi.$$

On the other hand, Theorem 278 yields

$$\sum_{n=1}^{x+1} [|\mathfrak{f}(n)|, 0] = \sum_{n=1}^{x} [|\mathfrak{f}(n)|, 0] + [|\mathfrak{f}(x+1)|, 0]$$

$$= [\Xi_1, 0] + [|\mathfrak{f}(x+1)|, 0] = [\Xi_1 + |\mathfrak{f}(x+1)|, 0+0] = [\Xi, 0].$$

Therefore Ξ satisfies the requirements in the case of $x+1$; hence $x+1$ belongs to $\mathfrak{M}$, and Theorem 287 is proved.

Theorem 288: *If* $\mathfrak{f}(n)$ *is defined for* $n \leqq x$, *then*

$$\left[\left|\prod_{n=1}^{x} \mathfrak{f}(n)\right|, 0\right] = \prod_{n=1}^{x} [|\mathfrak{f}(n)|, 0].$$

Proof: Let $\mathfrak{M}$ be the set of all x for which this holds.

I) If $\mathfrak{f}(1)$ is defined, then

$$\left[\left|\prod_{n=1}^{1} \mathfrak{f}(n)\right|, 0\right] = [|\mathfrak{f}(1)|, 0] = \prod_{n=1}^{1} [|\mathfrak{f}(n)|, 0].$$

Hence 1 belongs to $\mathfrak{M}$.

II) Let x belong to $\mathfrak{M}$. If $\mathfrak{f}(n)$ is defined for $n \leqq x+1$, then we have by Theorems 278 and 268 that

$$\prod_{n=1}^{x+1} [|\mathfrak{f}(n)|, 0] = \prod_{n=1}^{x} [|\mathfrak{f}(n)|, 0] \cdot [|\mathfrak{f}(x+1)|, 0]$$

$$= \left[\left|\prod_{n=1}^{x} \mathfrak{f}(n)\right|, 0\right] \cdot [|\mathfrak{f}(x+1)|, 0]$$

$$= \left[\left|\prod_{n=1}^{x} \mathfrak{f}(n)\right| \cdot |\mathfrak{f}(x+1)| - 0 \cdot 0, \left|\prod_{n=1}^{x} \mathfrak{f}(n)\right| \cdot 0 + 0 \cdot |\mathfrak{f}(x+1)|\right]$$

$$= \left[\left|\prod_{n=1}^{x} \mathfrak{f}(n)\right| \cdot |\mathfrak{f}(x+1)|, 0\right] = \left[\left|\prod_{n=1}^{x} \mathfrak{f}(n) \cdot \mathfrak{f}(x+1)\right|, 0\right]$$

$$= \left[\left|\prod_{n=1}^{x+1} \mathfrak{f}(n)\right|, 0\right],$$

so that $x+1$ belongs to $\mathfrak{M}$, and Theorem 288 is proved.

Theorem 289: *If* $\mathfrak{f}(n)$ *is defined for* $n \leqq x$, *then*

$$\prod_{n=1}^{x} \mathfrak{f}(n) = \mathfrak{n}$$

if and only if there exists an $n \leqq x$ *such that*

$$\mathfrak{f}(n) = \mathfrak{n}.$$

Proof: Let $\mathfrak{M}$ be the set of all x for which this holds.

I)

$$\prod_{n=1}^{1} \mathfrak{f}(n) = \mathfrak{n}$$

is identical with

$$\mathfrak{f}(1) = \mathfrak{n}.$$

Hence 1 belongs to $\mathfrak{M}$.

II) Let x belong to $\mathfrak{M}$.

$$\prod_{n=1}^{x+1} \mathfrak{f}(n) = \mathfrak{n}$$

means

$$\prod_{n=1}^{x} \mathfrak{f}(n) \cdot \mathfrak{f}(x+1) = \mathfrak{n};$$

by Theorem 221, a necessary and sufficient condition for this is that

$$\prod_{n=1}^{x} \mathfrak{f}(n) = \mathfrak{n} \quad \text{or} \quad \mathfrak{f}(x+1) = \mathfrak{n},$$

i.e. (since x belongs to $\mathfrak{M}$) that

$$\mathfrak{f}(n) = \mathfrak{n} \text{ for some } n \leqq x \text{ or for } n = x + 1.$$

Hence $x + 1$ belongs to $\mathfrak{M}$, and Theorem 289 is proved.

§ 9

Powers

In this section, small italic letters will stand for integers.

Definition 71:

$$\mathfrak{x}^x = \begin{cases} \prod_{n=1}^{x} \mathfrak{x} & \textit{for } x > 0, \\ \mathfrak{e} & \textit{for } \mathfrak{x} \neq \mathfrak{n},\ x = 0, \\ \dfrac{\mathfrak{e}}{\mathfrak{x}^{|x|}} & \textit{for } \mathfrak{x} \neq \mathfrak{n},\ x < 0. \end{cases}$$

(To be read "$\mathfrak{x}$ to the x.") Thus $\mathfrak{x}^x$ is always defined except when

$$\mathfrak{x} = \mathfrak{n},\ x \leqq 0.$$

Note that if

$$\mathfrak{x} \neq \mathfrak{n},\ x < 0,$$

then we have, by the first line of Definition 71 and by Theorem 289, that

$$\mathfrak{x}^{|x|} \neq \mathfrak{n},$$

so that $\frac{\mathfrak{e}}{\mathfrak{x}^{|x|}}$ is then meaningful.

Theorem 290: *If*

$$\mathfrak{x} \neq \mathfrak{n}$$

then

$$\mathfrak{x}^x \neq \mathfrak{n}.$$

Proof: For $x > 0$ this follows from Theorem 289; for $x = 0$, from the definition; and for $x < 0$, from

$$\mathfrak{x}^x \mathfrak{x}^{|x|} \neq \mathfrak{n}.$$

Theorem 291: $$\mathfrak{x}^1 = \mathfrak{x}.$$

Proof: $$\mathfrak{x}^1 = \prod_{n=1}^{1} \mathfrak{x} = \mathfrak{x}.$$

Theorem 292: *Let*

$$x > 0$$

or

$$\mathfrak{x} \neq \mathfrak{n},\ \mathfrak{y} \neq \mathfrak{n}.$$

Then

$$(\mathfrak{x}\mathfrak{y})^x = \mathfrak{x}^x \mathfrak{y}^x.$$

Preliminary Remark: Both sides are certainly meaningful; for if $x \leqq 0$, then

$$\mathfrak{x}\mathfrak{y} \neq \mathfrak{n}.$$

Proof: 1) For fixed $\mathfrak{x}$, $\mathfrak{y}$, let $\mathfrak{M}$ be the set of all $x > 0$ for which

$$(\mathfrak{x}\mathfrak{y})^x = \mathfrak{x}^x \mathfrak{y}^x.$$

I) By Theorem 291, we have

$$(\mathfrak{x}\mathfrak{y})^1 = \mathfrak{x}\mathfrak{y} = \mathfrak{x}^1 \mathfrak{y}^1,$$

so that 1 belongs to $\mathfrak{M}$.

II) If x belongs to $\mathfrak{M}$, then

$$(\mathfrak{x}\mathfrak{y})^{x+1} = \prod_{n=1}^{x+1} (\mathfrak{x}\mathfrak{y}) = \prod_{n=1}^{x} (\mathfrak{x}\mathfrak{y}) \cdot (\mathfrak{x}\mathfrak{y}) = (\mathfrak{x}^x \mathfrak{y}^x)(\mathfrak{x}\mathfrak{y}) = (\mathfrak{x}^x \mathfrak{x})(\mathfrak{y}^x \mathfrak{y})$$

$$= \left(\prod_{n=1}^{x} \mathfrak{x} \cdot \mathfrak{x}\right)\left(\prod_{n=1}^{x} \mathfrak{y} \cdot \mathfrak{y}\right) = \prod_{n=1}^{x+1} \mathfrak{x} \cdot \prod_{n=1}^{x+1} \mathfrak{y} = \mathfrak{x}^{x+1} \mathfrak{y}^{x+1},$$

so that $x + 1$ belongs to $\mathfrak{M}$.

Thus if $x > 0$, then we always have

$$(\mathfrak{x}\mathfrak{y})^x = \mathfrak{x}^x \mathfrak{y}^x.$$

2) Let

$$x = 0, \quad \mathfrak{x} \neq \mathfrak{n}, \quad \mathfrak{y} \neq \mathfrak{n}.$$

Then

$$(\mathfrak{x}\mathfrak{y})^x = \mathfrak{e} = \mathfrak{e}\mathfrak{e} = \mathfrak{x}^x \mathfrak{y}^x.$$

3) Let

$$x < 0, \quad \mathfrak{x} \neq \mathfrak{n}, \quad \mathfrak{y} \neq \mathfrak{n}.$$

By 1), we have

$$(\mathfrak{x}\mathfrak{y})^{|x|} = \mathfrak{x}^{|x|} \mathfrak{y}^{|x|},$$

$$\frac{\mathfrak{e}}{(\mathfrak{x}\mathfrak{y})^{|x|}} = \frac{\mathfrak{e}}{\mathfrak{x}^{|x|} \mathfrak{y}^{|x|}} = \frac{\mathfrak{e}}{\mathfrak{x}^{|x|}} \cdot \frac{\mathfrak{e}}{\mathfrak{y}^{|x|}},$$

$$(\mathfrak{x}\mathfrak{y})^x = \mathfrak{x}^x \mathfrak{y}^x.$$

Theorem 293:

$$\mathfrak{e}^x = \mathfrak{e}.$$

Proof: By Theorem 292, we have

$$\mathfrak{e}^x \mathfrak{e} = \mathfrak{e}^x = (\mathfrak{e}\mathfrak{e})^x = \mathfrak{e}^x \mathfrak{e}^x,$$

$$\mathfrak{n} = \mathfrak{e}^x \mathfrak{e}^x - \mathfrak{e}^x \mathfrak{e} = \mathfrak{e}^x (\mathfrak{e}^x - \mathfrak{e}),$$

so that, by Theorems 290 and 221,

$$\mathfrak{e}^x - \mathfrak{e} = \mathfrak{n},$$

$$\mathfrak{e}^x = \mathfrak{e}.$$

Theorem 294: *Let*

$$x > 0, \quad y > 0$$

or

$$\mathfrak{x} \neq \mathfrak{n}.$$

Then

$$\mathfrak{x}^x \mathfrak{x}^y = \mathfrak{x}^{x+y}.$$

Proof: 1) Let

$$x > 0, \quad y > 0.$$

Then, by Theorem 281,

$$\mathfrak{x}^x \mathfrak{x}^y = \prod_{n=1}^{x} \mathfrak{x} \cdot \prod_{n=1}^{y} \mathfrak{x} = \prod_{n=1}^{x+y} \mathfrak{x} = \mathfrak{x}^{x+y}.$$

2) Let

$$\mathfrak{x} \neq \mathfrak{n}$$

but not at the same time

$$x > 0, \; y > 0.$$

α) Let

$$x < 0, \; y < 0.$$

Then, by 1),

$$\mathfrak{x}^{|x|} \mathfrak{x}^{|y|} = \mathfrak{x}^{|x|+|y|} = \mathfrak{x}^{|x+y|},$$

$$\mathfrak{x}^x \mathfrak{x}^y = \frac{\mathfrak{e}}{\mathfrak{x}^{|x|}} \cdot \frac{\mathfrak{e}}{\mathfrak{x}^{|y|}} = \frac{\mathfrak{e}}{\mathfrak{x}^{|x|} \mathfrak{x}^{|y|}} = \frac{\mathfrak{e}}{\mathfrak{x}^{|x+y|}} = \mathfrak{x}^{x+y}.$$

β) Let

$$x > 0, \; y < 0.$$

Then

$$\mathfrak{x}^x \mathfrak{x}^y = \mathfrak{x}^x \frac{\mathfrak{e}}{\mathfrak{x}^{|y|}} = \frac{\mathfrak{x}^x}{\mathfrak{x}^{|y|}}.$$

A) If

$$x > |y|$$

then, by 1),

$$\frac{\mathfrak{x}^x}{\mathfrak{x}^{|y|}} = \frac{\mathfrak{x}^{|y|} \mathfrak{x}^{x-|y|}}{\mathfrak{x}^{|y|}} = \mathfrak{x}^{x-|y|} = \mathfrak{x}^{x+y}.$$

B) If

$$x = |y|$$

then

$$\frac{\mathfrak{x}^x}{\mathfrak{x}^{|y|}} = \mathfrak{e} = \mathfrak{x}^0 = \mathfrak{x}^{x+y}.$$

C) If

$$x < |y|$$

then, by 1),

$$\frac{\mathfrak{x}^x}{\mathfrak{x}^{|y|}} = \frac{\mathfrak{x}^x \mathfrak{e}}{\mathfrak{x}^x \mathfrak{x}^{|y|-x}} = \frac{\mathfrak{e}}{\mathfrak{x}^{|y|-x}} = \mathfrak{x}^{x-|y|} = \mathfrak{x}^{x+y}.$$

γ) Let

$$x < 0,\ y > 0.$$

Then, by β),

$$\mathfrak{x}^x \mathfrak{x}^y = \mathfrak{x}^y \mathfrak{x}^x = \mathfrak{x}^{y+x} = \mathfrak{x}^{x+y}.$$

δ) Let

$$x = 0.$$

Then

$$\mathfrak{x}^x \mathfrak{x}^y = \mathfrak{e}\mathfrak{x}^y = \mathfrak{x}^y = \mathfrak{x}^{0+y} = \mathfrak{x}^{x+y}.$$

ε) Let

$$x \neq 0,\quad y = 0.$$

Then, by δ),

$$\mathfrak{x}^x \mathfrak{x}^y = \mathfrak{x}^y \mathfrak{x}^x = \mathfrak{x}^{y+x} = \mathfrak{x}^{x+y}.$$

Theorem 295: *If*

$$\mathfrak{x} \neq \mathfrak{n}$$

then

$$\frac{\mathfrak{x}^x}{\mathfrak{x}^y} = \mathfrak{x}^{x-y}.$$

Proof: By Theorem 294, we have

$$\mathfrak{x}^{x-y}\mathfrak{x}^y = \mathfrak{x}^{(x-y)+y} = \mathfrak{x}^x;$$

by Theorem 290, we have

$$\mathfrak{x}^y \neq \mathfrak{n},$$

hence

$$\frac{\mathfrak{x}^x}{\mathfrak{x}^y} = \mathfrak{x}^{x-y}.$$

Theorem 296: *If*

$$\mathfrak{x} \neq \mathfrak{n}$$

then

$$\frac{\mathfrak{e}}{\mathfrak{x}^x} = \mathfrak{x}^{-x}.$$

Proof: By Theorem 295, we have

$$\frac{\mathfrak{e}}{\mathfrak{x}^x} = \frac{\mathfrak{x}^0}{\mathfrak{x}^x} = \mathfrak{x}^{0-x} = \mathfrak{x}^{-x}.$$

Theorem 297: *Let*

$$x > 0,\ y > 0$$

or

$$\mathfrak{x} \neq \mathfrak{n}.$$

Then

$$(\mathfrak{x}^x)^y = \mathfrak{x}^{xy}.$$

Proof: 1) Let

$$\mathfrak{x} = \mathfrak{n},\quad x > 0,\quad y > 0.$$

Then we have by Theorem 289 that

$$(\mathfrak{x}^x)^y = (\mathfrak{n}^x)^y = \mathfrak{n}^y = \mathfrak{n} = \mathfrak{n}^{xy} = \mathfrak{x}^{xy}.$$

2) Let

$$\mathfrak{x} \neq \mathfrak{n}.$$

a) For fixed $\mathfrak{x}$, x, let $\mathfrak{M}$ be the set of all $y > 0$ such that

$$(\mathfrak{x}^x)^y = \mathfrak{x}^{xy}.$$

I) $$(\mathfrak{x}^x)^1 = \mathfrak{x}^x = \mathfrak{x}^{x \cdot 1};$$

hence 1 belongs to $\mathfrak{M}$.

II) Let y belong to $\mathfrak{M}$. Then we have by Theorem 294 that

$$(\mathfrak{x}^x)^{y+1} = (\mathfrak{x}^x)^y (\mathfrak{x}^x)^1 = \mathfrak{x}^{xy}\mathfrak{x}^x = \mathfrak{x}^{xy+x} = \mathfrak{x}^{x(y+1)},$$

so that $y + 1$ belongs to $\mathfrak{M}$.

Therefore the assertion is true for $y > 0$.

b) Let

$$y = 0.$$

Then

$$(\mathfrak{x}^x)^y = \mathfrak{e} = \mathfrak{x}^{xy}.$$

c) Let

$$y < 0.$$

Then, by a),

$$(\mathfrak{x}^x)^{|y|} = \mathfrak{x}^{x|y|},$$

so that, by Theorem 296 and by a),

$$(\mathfrak{x}^x)^y = \frac{\mathfrak{e}}{(\mathfrak{x}^x)^{-y}} = \frac{\mathfrak{e}}{(\mathfrak{x}^x)^{|y|}} = \frac{\mathfrak{e}}{\mathfrak{x}^{x|y|}} = \mathfrak{x}^{-(x|y|)} = \mathfrak{x}^{xy}.$$

§ 10

Incorporation of the Real Numbers into the System of Complex Numbers

Theorem 298:

$$[\Xi + H, 0] = [\Xi, 0] + [H, 0];$$
$$[\Xi - H, 0] = [\Xi, 0] - [H, 0];$$
$$[\Xi H, 0] = [\Xi, 0][H, 0];$$
$$\left[\frac{\Xi}{H}, 0\right] = \frac{[\Xi, 0]}{[H, 0]}, \quad \textit{if } H \neq 0;$$
$$[-\Xi, 0] = -[\Xi, 0];$$
$$|[\Xi, 0]| = |\Xi|.$$

Proof: 1) $[\Xi, 0] + [H, 0] = [\Xi + H, 0 + 0] = [\Xi + H, 0]$.

2) $[\Xi, 0] - [H, 0] = [\Xi - H, 0 - 0] = [\Xi - H, 0]$.

3) $[\Xi, 0][H, 0] = [\Xi H - 0 \cdot 0, \Xi \cdot 0 + 0 \cdot H] = [\Xi H, 0]$.

4) By 3) we have, if $H \neq 0$, that

$$[H, 0]\left[\frac{\Xi}{H}, 0\right] = \left[H\frac{\Xi}{H}, 0\right] = [\Xi, 0],$$

$$\frac{[\Xi, 0]}{[H, 0]} = \left[\frac{\Xi}{H}, 0\right].$$

5) $$-[\Xi, 0] = [-\Xi, -0] = [-\Xi, 0].$$

6) $|\Xi| = \sqrt{|\Xi||\Xi|} = \sqrt{\Xi\Xi} = \sqrt{\Xi\Xi + 0 \cdot 0} = |[\Xi, 0]|$.

Theorem 299: *The complex numbers of the form* $[x, 0]$ *satisfy the five axioms of the natural numbers if the role of* 1 *is assigned to* $[1, 0]$ *and if we set*

$$[x, 0]' = [x', 0].$$

Proof: Denote the set of all $[x, 0]$ by $[\mathfrak{Z}]$.

1) $[1,0]$ belongs to $[\mathfrak{Z}]$.

2) If $[x, 0]$ belongs to $[\mathfrak{Z}]$ then so does $[x, 0]'$.

3) We always have

$$x' \neq 1,$$

hence

$$[x', 0] \neq [1, 0],$$
$$[x, 0]' \neq [1, 0].$$

4) If

$$[x, 0]' = [y, 0]'$$

then

$$[x', 0] = [y', 0],$$
$$x' = y',$$
$$x = y,$$
$$[x, 0] = [y, 0].$$

5) Let a set $[\mathfrak{M}]$ of numbers from $[\mathfrak{Z}]$ have the following properties:

I) $[1, 0]$ belongs to $[\mathfrak{M}]$.

II) If $[x, 0]$ belongs $[\mathfrak{M}]$ then so does $[x, 0]'$.

Now denote by $\mathfrak{M}$ the set of all x for which $[x, 0]$ belongs to $[\mathfrak{M}]$. Then 1 belongs to $\mathfrak{M}$, and if x belongs to $\mathfrak{M}$ then so does x'. Therefore every positive integer x belongs to $\mathfrak{M}$, so that every $[x, 0]$ belongs to $[\mathfrak{M}]$.

Sum, difference, product, and quotient (whenever it exists) of two $[\Xi, 0]$ correspond, by Theorem 298, to the earlier concepts, as do also the symbols $-[\Xi, 0]$ and $|[\Xi, 0]|$; moreover, we may define

$$[\Xi, 0] > [H, 0] \text{ if } \Xi > H,$$
$$[\Xi, 0] < [H, 0] \text{ if } \Xi < H.$$

Thus the complex numbers $[\Xi, 0]$ have all the properties which we have proved, in Chapter 4, attach to the real numbers; the numbers $[x, 0]$, in particular, have all the properties that have been established for the positive integers.

Therefore, we throw out the real numbers and replace them by the corresponding complex numbers $[\Xi, 0]$, so that we need no longer speak in terms of any but complex numbers. (However, the real numbers survive—in pairs—in the concept of complex number.)

Definition 72: *The symbol* Ξ (now freed of its previous meaning) *will denote the complex number* $[\Xi, 0]$ *to which we also transfer the name "real number." Similarly,* $[\Xi, 0]$ *will now be called an integer if* Ξ *is an integer; a rational number if* Ξ *is rational; an irrational number if* Ξ *is irrational; a positive number if* Ξ *is positive; a negative number if* Ξ *is negative.*

Thus we write, for instance, 0 in place of $\mathfrak{n}$, and 1 in place of $\mathfrak{e}$.

Now we may denote the complex numbers by small or by capital letters of any alphabet whatsoever (even mixing alphabets if we wish to). However, the following specific number is usually denoted by a (specific) small italic letter, on the basis of

Definition 73:
$$i = [0, 1].$$

Theorem 300:
$$ii = -1.$$

Proof:
$$ii = [0, 1][0, 1] = [0\cdot 0-1\cdot 1,\ 0\cdot 1+1\cdot 0]$$
$$= [-1, 0] = -1.$$

Theorem 301: *For real* u_1, u_2, *we have*
$$u_1+u_2 i = [u_1, u_2].$$
Hence for every complex number x, *there exists exactly one pair of real numbers* u_1, u_2 *such that*
$$x = u_1+u_2 i.$$

Proof: For real u_1, u_2, we have
$$u_1+u_2 i = [u_1, 0]+[u_2, 0][0, 1] = [u_1, 0]+[u_2\cdot 0-0\cdot 1,\ u_2\cdot 1+0\cdot 0]$$
$$= [u_1, 0]+[0, u_2] = [u_1, u_2].$$

By Theorem 301, the symbol [ ] has become superfluous; the complex numbers are simply the numbers $u_1 + u_2 i$, where u_1 and u_2 are real. To equal (unequal) pairs u_1, u_2 correspond equal (unequal) numbers, and the sum, difference, and product of two complex numbers $u_1 + u_2 i$, $v_1 + v_2 i$ (where u_1, u_2, v_1, v_2 are real) are constructed by means of the formulas
$$(u_1+u_2 i)+(v_1+v_2 i) = (u_1+v_1)+(u_2+v_2)i,$$
$$(u_1+u_2 i)-(v_1+v_2 i) = (u_1-v_1)+(u_2-v_2)i,$$
$$(u_1+u_2 i)(v_1+v_2 i) = (u_1 v_1-u_2 v_2)+(u_1 v_2+u_2 v_1)i.$$
We need not even memorize these formulas, as long as we remember that the laws for operating with real numbers remain valid and that Theorem 300 holds; then we can simply calculate as follows:
$$(u_1+u_2 i)+(v_1+v_2 i) = (u_1+v_1)+(u_2 i+v_2 i) = (u_1+v_1)+(u_2+v_2)i,$$
$$(u_1+u_2 i)-(v_1+v_2 i) = (u_1-v_1)+(u_2 i-v_2 i) = (u_1-v_1)+(u_2-v_2)i,$$
$$\begin{aligned}(u_1+u_2 i)(v_1+v_2 i) &= (u_1+u_2 i)v_1+(u_1+u_2 i)v_2 i\\ &= u_1 v_1+u_2 i v_1+u_1 v_2 i+u_2 i v_2 i\\ &= u_1 v_1+u_2 v_1 i+u_1 v_2 i+u_2 v_2 ii\\ &= u_1 v_1+u_2 v_1 i+u_1 v_2 i+u_2 v_2(-1)\\ &= (u_1 v_1-u_2 v_2)+(u_1 v_2+u_2 v_1)i.\end{aligned}$$

As to division, calculation yields, provided that v_1 and v_2 are not both zero, that

$$\frac{u_1 + u_2 i}{v_1 + v_2 i} = \frac{(u_1 + u_2 i)(v_1 - v_2 i)}{(v_1 + v_2 i)(v_1 - v_2 i)} = \frac{(u_1 v_1 + u_2 v_2) + (-(u_1 v_2) + u_2 v_1) i}{(v_1 v_1 + v_2 v_2) + (-(v_1 v_2) + v_2 v_1) i}$$

$$= \frac{(u_1 v_1 + u_2 v_2) + (-(u_1 v_2) + u_2 v_1) i}{v_1 v_1 + v_2 v_2} = \frac{u_1 v_1 + u_2 v_2}{v_1 v_1 + v_2 v_2} + \frac{-(u_1 v_2) + u_2 v_1}{v_1 v_1 + v_2 v_2} i$$

is the canonical representation in the sense of Theorem 301.

INDEX

CHELSEA

SCIENTIFIC

BOOKS

STRING FIGURES, and other monographs

By BALL, CAJORI, CARSLAW, and PETERSEN

FOUR VOLUMES IN ONE:
String Figures, *by W. W. Rouse Ball;*

The Elements of Non-Euclidean Plane Geometry, *by H. S. Carslaw;*

A History of the Logarithmic Slide Rule, *by F. Cajori;*

Methods and Theories for the Solution of Problems of Geometrical Construction, *by J. Petersen*

—528 pp. 5¼x8. [130] Four vols. in one. **$3.95**

THÉORIE DES OPÉRATIONS LINÉAIRES

By S. BANACH

—1933. xii + 250 pp. 5¼x8¼. [110] **$3.95**

THEORIE DER FUNKTIONEN MEHRERER KOMPLEXER VERÄNDERLICHEN

By H. BEHNKE and P. THULLEN

—(Ergeb. der Math.) 1934. vii+115 pp. 5½x8½. [68] **$3.25**

CONFORMAL MAPPING

By L. BIEBERBACH

"The first book in English to give an elementary, readable account of the Riemann Mapping Theorem and the distortion theorems and uniformisation problem with which it is connected. . . . The fourth presented in very attractive and readable form."
—*Math. Gazette.*

". . . thorough and painstaking . . . lucid and clear and well arranged . . . an excellent text."
—*Bulletin of the A. M. S.*

Engineers will profitably use this book for its accurate exposition."—*Appl. Mechanics Reviews.*

—1952. vi + 234 pp. 4½x6½. [90] **$2.50**

BASIC GEOMETRY

By G. D. BIRKHOFF and R. BEATLEY

A highly recommended high-school text by two eminent scholars.

—Third edition. 1959. 294 pp. 5¼x8. [120] **$3.95**

ALMOST PERIODIC FUNCTIONS

By H. BOHR

Translated by H. COHN. From the famous series *Ergebnisse der Mathematik und ihrer Grenzgebiete,* a beautiful exposition of the theory of Almost Periodic Functions written by the creator of that theory.

—1951. 120 pp. 6x9. Lithotyped. German edition was $4.50.
[27] **$2.50**

THE CALCULUS OF FINITE DIFFERENCES

By G. BOOLE

A standard work on the subject of finite differences and difference equations by one of the seminal minds in the field of finite mathematics.

Some of the topics covered are: *Interpolation, Finite Integration, Summation of Series, General Theory of Difference and Differential Equations of First Order, Linear DEqns with Variable Coefficients, Linear DEqns, Geometrical Applications.*

Numerous exercises with answers.

—Fourth edition. 1958. xii+336 pp. 5x8. [121] Cloth **$3.95**
[148] Paper **$1.39**

A TREATISE ON DIFFERENTIAL EQUATIONS

By G. BOOLE

Including the Supplementary Volume.

—Fifth edition. 1959. xxiv + 735 pp. 5¼x8. [128] **$4.95**

THEORY OF FUNCTIONS

By C. CARATHÉODORY

Translated by F. STEINHARDT. The recent, and already famous textbook, *Funktionentheorie.*

Partial Contents: **Part One.** Chap. I. Algebra of Complex Numbers II. Geometry of Complex Numbers. III. Euclidean, Spherical, and Non-Euclidean Geometry. **Part Two.** Theorems from Point Set Theory and Topology. Chap. I. Sequences and Continuous Complex Functions. II. Curves and Regions. III. Line Integrals. **Part Three.** Analytic Functions. Chap. I. Foundations. II. The Maximum-modulus principle. III. Poisson Integral and Harmonic Functions. IV. Meromorphic Functions. **Part Four.** Generation of Analytic Functions by Limiting Processes. Chap. I. Uniform Convergence. II. Normal Families of Meromorphic Functions. III. Power Series. IV. Partial Fraction Decomposition and the Calculus of Residues. **Part Five.** Special Functions. Chap. I. The Exponential Function and the Trigonometric Functions. II. Logarithmic Function. III. Bernoulli Numbers and the Gamma Function.

Vol. II.: **Part Six.** Foundations of Geometric Function Theory. Chap. I. Bounded Functions. II. Conformal Mapping. III. The Mapping of the Boundary. **Part Seven.** The Triangle Function and Picard's Theorem. Chap. I. Functions of Several Complex Variables. II. Conformal Mapping of Circular-Arc Triangles. III. The Schwarz Triangle Functions and the Modular Function. IV. Essential Singularities and Picard's Theorems.

"A book by a master . . . Carathéodory himself regarded [it] as his finest achievement . . . written from a catholic point of view."—*Bulletin of A.M.S.*

—Vol. I. Second edition. 1958. 310 pp. 6x9. [97] **$4.95**
—Vol. II. 1954. 220 pp. 6x9. [106] **$4.95**

HISTORY OF THE THEORY OF NUMBERS

By L. E. DICKSON

"A monumental work . . . Dickson always has in mind the needs of the investigator . . . The author has [often] expressed in a nut-shell the main results of a long and involved paper *in a much clearer way than the writer of the article did himself.* The ability to reduce complicated mathematical arguments to simple and elementary terms is highly developed in Dickson."—*Bulletin of A. M. S.*

—Vol. I (Divisibility and Primality) xii+486 pp. Vol. II (Diophantine Analysis) xxv+803 pp. Vol. III (Quadratic and Higher Forms) v+313 pp. [86] Three vol. set **$19.95**

THE INTEGRAL CALCULUS

By J. W. EDWARDS

A leisurely, immensely detailed, textbook of over 1,900 pages, rich in illustrative examples and manipulative techniques and containing much interesting material that must of necessity be omitted from less comprehensive works.

There are forty large chapters in all. The earlier cover a leisurely and a more-than-usually-detailed treatment of all the elementary standard topics. Later chapters include: Jacobian Elliptic Functions, Weierstrassian Elliptic Functions, Evaluation of Definite Integrals, Harmonic Analysis, Calculus of Variations, etc. Every chapter contains many exercises (with solutions).

—2 vols. 1,922 pp. 5x8. Originally published at $31.50 the set. [102], [105] Each volume **$7.50**

AUTOMORPHIC FUNCTIONS

By L. R. FORD

"Comprehensive . . . remarkably clear and explicit."—*Bulletin of the A. M. S.*

—2nd ed. (Cor. repr.) x+333 pp. 5⅜x8. [85] **$4.95**

TEXTBOOK OF ALGEBRA

By G. CHRYSTAL

The usefulness, both as a textbook and as a work of reference, of this charming classic is attested to by the number of editions it has run through—the present being the sixth. Its richness of content can be only appreciated by an examination of the twelve-hundred-page book itself. **Thousands of valuable exercises (with solutions).**

6th ed. 2 Vols. 1235 pages. 5⅜x8. [84] Each volume **$2.95**

RUSSIAN MATHEMATICAL BIBLIOGRAPHY

By G. E. FORSYTHE

A bibliography of Russian Mathematics Books for the past quarter century. Supplements may be issued. Added subject index.

—1956, 106 pp. 5x8. [111] **$3.95**

THE THEORY OF MATRICES

By F. R. GANTMACHER

Translated from the Russian, with further revisions by the Author.

This treatise by one of Russia's leading mathematicians gives, in easily accessible form, a coherent account of matrix theory with a view to applications in mathematics, theoretical physics, statistics, electrical engineering, etc. The individual chapters have been kept as far as possble independent of each other, so that the reader acquainted with the contents of Chapter I can proceed immediately to the chapters that especially interest him. Much of the material has been available until now only in the periodical literature.

Partial Contents. VOL ONE. I. Matrices and Matrix Operations. II. The Algorithm of Gauss and Applications. III. Linear Operators in an n-Dimensional Vector Space. IV. Characteristic Polynomial and Minimal Polynomial of a Matrix (Generalized Bézout Theorem, Method of Faddeev for Simultaneous Computation of Coefficients of Characteristic Polynomial and Adjoint Matrix, ...). V. Functions of Matrices (Various Forms of the Definition, Components, Application to Integration of System of Linear Differential Eqns, Stability of Motion, ...). VI. Equivalent Transformations of Polynomial Matrices; Analytic Theory of Elementary Divisors. VII. The Structure of a Linear Operator in an n-Dimensional Space (Minimal Polynomial, Congruence, Factor Space, Jordan Form, Krylov's Method of Transforming Secular Eqn, ...). VIII. Matrix Equations (Matrix Polynomial Eqns, Roots and Logarithm of Matrices, ...). IX. Linear Operators in a Unitary Space. X. Quadratic and Hermitian Forms.

VOLUME TWO. XI. Complex Symmetric, Skew-symmetric, and Orthogonal Matrices. XII. Singular Pencils of Matrices. XIII. Matrices with Non-Negative Elements (General Properties, Spectral Properties, Reducible Matrices, Primitive and Imprimitive Matrices, Stochastic Matrices, Limiting Probabilities for Homogeneous Markov Chain, Totally Non-Negative Matrices, Oscillatory Matrices...). XIV. Applications of the Theory of Matrices to the Investigation of Systems of Linear Differential Equations (Systems with Variable Coefficients, Lyapunov Transformations, Reducible Systems, Erugin's Theorem, Multiplicative Integral, Volterra's Calculus, Differential Systems in Complex Domain, Analytic Functions of Several Matrices, The Research of Lappo-Danilevskii, ...). XV. The Problem of Routh-Hurwitz and Related Questions (Routh's Algorithm, Lyapunov's Theorem, Method of Quadratic Forms, Infinite Hankel Matrices of Finite Rank, Supplements to Routh-Hurwitz Theorem, Stability Criterion of Liénard and Chipart, Properties of Hurwitz Polynomials, Stieltjes' Theorem, Representation by Continued Fractions, Domain of Stability, Markov Parameters, Problem of Moments. Theorems of Markov and Chebyshev. Generalized Routh-Hurwitz Problem, ...). Bibliography.

—Vol. I. 1959. x + 374 pp. 6x9. [131] **$6.00**
—Vol. II. 1959. x + 277 pp. 6x9. [133] **$6.00**

INTRODUCTION TO HILBERT SPACE AND THE THEORY OF SPECTRAL MULTIPLICITY

By P. R. HALMOS

Prof. Halmos' latest book gives a clear, readable introductory treatment of Hilbert Space. The multiplicity theory of continuous spectra is treated, for the first time in English, in full generality.

—1957. 2nd. ed. (c. repr. of 1st ed.). 120 pp. 6x9. [82] **$3.25**

RAMANUJAN:
Twelve Lectures on His Life and Works

By G. H. HARDY

— viii + 236 pp. 6x9 [136] **$3.95**

GRUNDZÜGE DER MENGENLEHRE

By F. HAUSDORFF

Some of the topics in the Grundzüge omitted from later editions:

Symmetric Sets—Principle of Duality—most of the "Algebra" of Sets—most of the "Ordered Sets"—Partially Ordered Sets—Arbitrary Sets of Complexes—Normal Types—Initial and Final Ordering—Complexes of Real Numbers—General Topological Spaces—Euclidean Spaces—the Special Methods Applicable in the Euclidean plane—Jordan's separation Theorem—The Theory of Content and Measure—The Theory of the Lebesgue Integral.

—First edition. 484 pp. 5½x8¼. [61] **$4.95**

SET THEORY

By F. HAUSDORFF

Now for the first time available in English, Hausdorff's classic text-book has been an inspiration and a delight to those who have read it in the original German. The translation is from the Third (latest) German edition.

"We wish to state without qualification that this is an indispensable book for all those interested in the theory of sets and the allied branches of real variable theory."—*Bulletin of A. M. S.*

—Second ed. 352 pp. 6x9. [119] **$6.50**

PRINCIPLES OF MATHEMATICAL LOGIC

By D. HILBERT and W. ACKERMANN

The famous *Grundzüge der Theoretischen Logik* translated into English, with added notes and revisions by PROF. R. E. LUCE.

"The best textbook in a Western European language for a student wishing a fairly thorough treatment."—*Bulletin of the A. M. S.*

—1950-59. xii + 172 pp. 6x9. [69] **$3.75**

GEOMETRY AND THE IMAGINATION

By D. HILBERT and S. COHN-VOSSEN

The theme of this book is *insight.* Not merely proofs, but proofs that offer *insight*—intuitive understanding—into *why they are true.* Not merely properties of the hyperboloid or of Pascal's hexagon, but insight into *why they have these properties.* In this wide-ranging survey, one of the world's greatest and most original mathematicians uses insight as both his technique and his aim. Both the beginner and the mature mathematician will learn much from this fascinating treatise.

Translated from the German by P. NEMENYI.

CHAPTER HEADINGS: I. The Simplest Curves and surfaces. II. Regular Systems of Points. III. Projective Configurations. IV. Differential Geometry. V. Kinematics. VI. Topology.

"A mathematical classic . . . The purpose is to make the reader *see* and *feel* the proofs."—*Science.*

" A fascinating tour of the 20th-century mathematical zoo."—*Scientific American.*

"Students . . . will experience the sensation of being taken into the friendly confidence of a great mathematician and being shown the **real significance** of things."—*Science Progress.*

"A glance down the index (*twenty-five columns of it*) reveal the breadth of range:—

"Annulus; Atomic structure; Automorphic functions; Bubble, soap; Caustic Curve; Color problem; Density of packing, of circles; Four-dimensional space; Gears, hyperboloidal; Graphite; Lattices; Mapping; "Monkey Saddle"; Table salt; Zinc.

"These are but a few of the topics . . . The title evokes the imagination and the text must surely capture it."—*Math. Gazette.*

—1952. 358 pp. 6x9. **$6.00**

SQUARING THE CIRCLE, and other Monographs

By HOBSON, HUDSON, SINGH, and KEMPE

SQUARING THE CIRCLE, by Hobson. A fascinating and scholarly history of the number π.

RULER AND COMPASSES, by *Hudson.* "An analytical and geometrical investigation of how far Euclidean constructions can take us. It is as thoroughgoing as it is constructive."—*Sci. Monthly.*

THE THEORY AND CONSTRUCTION OF NON-DIFFERENTIABLE FUNCTIONS, by *Singh.* I. Functions Defined by Series. II. Functions Defined Geometrically. III. Functions Defined Arithmetically. IV. Properties of Non-Differentiable Functions.

HOW TO DRAW A STRAIGHT LINE, by *Kempe.* An intriguing monograph on linkages. Describes, among other things, a linkage that will trisect any angle.

"Intriguing, meaty."—*Scientific American.*

—388 pp. 4½x7½. Four vols. in one **$3.25**

DIFFERENTIAL AND INTEGRAL CALCULUS

By E. LANDAU

Landau's sparkling *Einführung* in English translation. Completely rigorous, completely self-contained, borrowing not even the fundamental theorem of algebra (of which it gives a rigorous elementary proof), it develops the entire calculus including Fourier series, starting only with the properties of the number system. A masterpiece of rigor and clarity.

—1950. 372 pp. 6x9. [78] **$6.00**

VORLESUNGEN ÜBER ZAHLENTHEORIE

By E. LANDAU

The various sections of this important work (Additive, Analytic, Geometric, and Algebraic Number Theory) can be read independently of one another.

—Vol. I, Pt. 2. *(Additive Number Theory) xii + 180 pp. Vol. II. (Analytical Number Theory and Geometrical Number Theory) viii + 308 pp. Vol. III. (Algebraic Number Theory and Fermat's Last Theorem) viii + 341 pp. 5¼x8¼. *(Vol I, Pt. 1 is issued as **Elementary Number Theory.**) Originally publ. at **$26.40**
[32] Three vols. in one **$14.00**

ELEMENTARY NUMBER THEORY

By E. LANDAU

The present work is a translation of Prof. Landau's famous *Elementare Zahlentheorie,* with added exercises by Prof. Paul T. Bateman.

PART ONE. Foundations of Number Theory. I. Divisors. II. Prime Numbers, Prime Factorization. III. G.C.D. IV. Number-theoretic Functions. V. Congruences. VI. Quadratic Residues. VII. Pell's Equation. PART TWO. Brun's Theorem and Dirichlet's Theorem. PART THREE. Decomposition into Two, Three, and Four Squares. I. Farey Fractions. II. Dec. into 2 Squares. III. Dec. into 4 Squares. IV. Dec. into 3 Squares. PART FOUR. Class Numbers of Binary Quadratic Forms. II. Classes of Forms. III. Finiteness of Class Number. IV. Primary Representation . . . VI. Gaussian Sums . . . IX. Final Formulas for Class Number.

EXERCISES for Parts One, Two, and Three.

—1958. 256 pp. 6x9. [125] **$4.95**

GRUNDLAGEN DER ANALYSIS

By E. LANDAU

The student who wishes to learn mathematical German will find this book ideally suited to his needs. *Less than fifty German words* will enable him to read the entire book with only an occasional glance at the vocabulary! [A *complete* German-English vocabulary has been added.]

—Orig. publ. at $4.00. [141] Paper **$1.95**

EINFÜHRUNG IN DIE ELEMENTARE UND ANALYTISCHE THEORIE DER ALGEBRAISCHEN ZAHLEN UND DER IDEALE

By E. LANDAU

—2nd ed. vii + 147 pp. 5½x8. [62] **$2.95**

TOPOLOGY

By S. LEFSCHETZ

CONTENTS: I. Elementary Combinatorial Theory of Complexes. II. Topological Invariance of Homology Characters. III. Manifolds and their Duality Theorems. IV. Intersections of Chains on a Manifold. V. Product Complexes. VI. Transformations of Manifolds, their Coincidences, Fixed Points. VII. Infinite Complexes. VIII. Applications to Analytical and Algebraic Varieties.

—2nd. ed. (Corr. repr. of 1st. ed.) x + 410 pp. 5¼x8¼. [116] **$4.95**

ELEMENTS OF ALGEBRA

By HOWARD LEVI

"This book is addressed to beginning students of mathematics. . . . The level of the book, however, is so unusually high, mathematically as well as pedagogically, that it merits the attention of professional mathematicians (as well as of professional pedagogues) interested in the wider dissemination of their subject among cultured people . . . **a closer approximation to the right way to teach mathematics to beginners than anything else now in existence."**—*Bulletin of the A. M. S.*

—Third ed. 1960. xi + 161 pp. 5⅜x8. [103] **$3.25**

LE CALCUL DES RÉSIDUS

By E. LINDELÖF

Important applications in a striking diversity of mathematical fields: statistics, number theory, the theory of Fourier series, the calculus of finite differences, mathematical physics and advanced calculus, as well as function theory itself.

—151 pp. 5½x8½. [34] **$3.25**

FUNCTIONS OF REAL VARIABLES
FUNCTIONS OF A COMPLEX VARIABLE

By W. F. OSGOOD

TWO VOLUMES IN ONE.

"*Well-organised courses, systematic, lucid, fundamental,* with many brief sets of appropriate exercises, and occasional suggestions for more extensive reading. The technical terms have been kept to a minimum, and have been clearly explained. The aim has been to develop the student's power and to furnish him with a substantial body of classic theorems, whose proofs illustrate the methods and whose results provide equipment for further progress."—*Bulletin of A. M. S.*

—676 pp. 5x8. 2 vols. in 1. [124] **$4.95**

KNOTENTHEORIE

By K. REIDEMEISTER

—(Ergeb. der Math.) 1932. 78 pp. 5½x8½. [40] **$2.25**

FOURIER SERIES

By W. ROGOSINSKI

Translated by H. COHN. Designed for beginners with no more background than a year of calculus, this text covers, nevertheless, an amazing amount of ground. It is suitable for self-study courses as well as classroom use.

"The field covered is extensive and the treatment is thoroughly modern in outlook . . . An admirable guide to the theory."—*Mathematical Gazette.*

—Second ed. 1959. vi + 176 pp. 4½x6½. [67] **$2.25**

CONIC SECTIONS

By G. SALMON

"The classic book on the subject, covering the whole ground and full of touches of genius."

—*Mathematical Association.*

—6th. ed. xv + 400 pp. 5¼x8¼. [99] Cloth **$3.25**
[98] Paper **$1.94**

ANALYTIC GEOMETRY OF THREE DIMENSIONS

By G. SALMON

A rich and detailed treatment by the author of *Conic Sections, Higher Plane Curves*, etc.

—Seventh edition. (V. 1.) 496 pp. 5x8. [122] **$4.95**

INTRODUCTION TO MODERN ALGEBRA AND MATRIX THEORY

By O. SCHREIER and E. SPERNER

An English translation of the revolutionary work, *Einführung in die Analytische Geometrie und Algebra*. Chapter Headings: I. Affine Space. Linear Equations. (Vector Spaces). II. Euclidean Space. Theory of Determinants. III. The Theory of Fields. Fundamental Theorem of Algebra. IV. Elements of Group Theory. V. Matrices and Linear Transformations. **The treatment of matrices is especially extensive.**

"Outstanding . . . good introduction . . . well suited for use as a text . . . Self-contained and each topic is painstakingly developed."

—*Mathematics Teacher.*

—Second ed. 1959. viii + 378 pp [80] **$6.00**